Also by Thomas Helm

HURRICANE COMING!

THE EVERGLADES: FLORIDA WONDERLAND

MONSTERS OF THE DEEP

SHARK!

TREASURE HUNTING AROUND THE WORLD

THE SEA LARK

A WORLD OF SNAKES

A
WORLD
OF
SNAKES

by

Thomas Helm

Illustrated with photographs and maps

DODD, MEAD & COMPANY

NEW YORK

Library of Congress Catalog Card Number: 65-27147
Printed in the United States of America
by The Cornwall Press, Inc., Cornwall, N.Y.

To my wife, Dorothy

ACKNOWLEDGMENTS

There is so much to know about snakes that no one could possibly learn it all in a lifetime. In writing this book the author called on numerous people for help in an effort to make it as technically accurate as possible. Sincere thanks for their valuable assistance go to the following:

George W. Gehres, Consultant of the Accident Prevention Program of the Florida State Board of Health, Jacksonville, Florida; William A. Haast, Director, Miami Serpentarium, Miami, Florida; R. Marlin Perkins, Director, St. Louis Zoological Park, St. Louis, Missouri; Ross Allen, President, Ross Allen's Reptile Institute, Silver Springs, Florida; LaMar Farnsworth, Director, Hogle Zoological Gardens, Salt Lake City, Utah; George D. Gross, M.D., Salt Lake City, Utah; Theron D. Carroll, Coordinator of Information and Education, Parks and Wildlife Department, Austin, Texas; Mrs. Eleanor E. Buckley, Wyeth Laboratories, Philadelphia, Pennsylvania; Henry M. Parrish, M.D., University of Missouri, Columbia, Missouri; Sherman A. Minton, Jr., M.D., Indiana University Medical Center, Indianapolis, Indiana; Herndon G. Dowling, Curator of Reptiles, New York Zoological Society, New York City; E. H. Bryan, Jr., Bernice P. Bishop Museum, Honolulu, Hawaii; Becton, Dickinson and

Company, Rutherford, New Jersey; Gokey Company, St. Paul, Minnesota and Cutter Laboratories, Berkeley, California.

A special note of thanks goes to Dick Bothwell who also enjoys investigating such creatures as snakes and alligators and to my long-time friend, Jack A. Holt, who has been with me on many snake-catching trips.

CONTENTS

ILLUSTRATIONS

Photographic supplement follows page 82

Rattlesnake mouth opened wide to expose fangs
Author's wife holding indigo snake
Author stepping on water moccasin to demonstrate snake-bite-
    proof boots

Maps: Approximate ranges of the four types of poisonous snakes
    found in the United States, pages 38-39
                    Copperheads   Rattlesnakes
                    Coral snakes   Water moccasins

A WORLD OF SNAKES

1

BIG SNAKES

The serpent holds the distinction of having in its clan the longest creatures that inhabit the earth today. This, of course, refers only to terrestrial animals and does not include such sea creatures as whales and giant squid.

The three truly giants of the snake world are the pythons, anacondas, and boa constrictors (*Constrictor constrictor*). Various species of pythons are widely distributed throughout Africa, Asia, India, and some of the islands of the South Pacific. The boa constrictors and the anacondas are restricted to the New World. Of the three heavyweights, the anaconda of tropical America holds the crown with reliable reports placing his length sometimes at nearly forty feet. The nearest contender is the reticulated python of Asia that reaches a length of approximately thirty feet. The smallest of the three, but the snake that has enjoyed the widest popularity in American fiction, and sometimes in supposedly factual articles, is the boa constrictor. The longest boa constrictor on record is an eighteen-foot six-inch specimen killed on the island of Trinidad during World War II.

Pythons, boa constrictors, and anacondas are all members

of the family Boidae. None possess venomous fangs; all kill their prey by constriction. The absence of poison, however, does not lessen the importance of the constrictor's mouth. The teeth are long, the jaws are powerful, and a bite from any of these great snakes can be as painful and as dangerous as a bite from a large dog.

There are persistent misconceptions about the size of the meals required by the large snakes, which have been exaggerated to include as food almost any animal except perhaps an elephant or a rhinoceros. Actually the diet of the large constrictors is on the whole limited to small animals such as monkeys, rodents, and occasionally birds. That humans are devoured is also just part of the folklore of jungle countries.

As might logically be expected, the size of the individual snake has much to do with the size of a potential meal it will tackle. For example, a ten-foot anaconda or python would be content to exist on a diet of monkeys, small pigs, and rats. The python that has grown to three times that length, however, would no hesitate to seize a hundred-pound wart hog or a young zebra, nor would a full-grown anaconda shy away from a tapir or large calf.

That constrictors kill their prey by crushing the animal with such force that most of the bones are broken is just another part of the myth. Whether it be a python, boa constrictor, or anaconda, the method of attack is the same. The snake waits along a jungle trail or in the shallows of a pool or stream. When an animal comes near, the snake lashes out and its jaws snap shut on the victim. Instantly, it begins to throw coil after coil around the animal's struggling body, and then these coils begin to contract. As the pressure increases, the animal is killed because it can no longer breathe.

After a constrictor is assured of the death of its victim, its method of swallowing is much the same as that of any other snake, from a corn snake engulfing a mouse to the rattler eating a rabbit. There is one exception in this process, however. The constrictor makes its task easier by stretching and elongating its meal before it begins the swallowing process. Solid portions, such as the head of a monkey, are not crushed, but when the swallowing is begun the head, along with the balance of the creature, slides down the snake's gullet where the powerful digestive juices in the stomach quickly disintegrate hide, hair, and bone.

Snakes make full use of every morsel of food they eat. When the meal has not been hearty, the snake may rest for only a few days between hunting expeditions. But an anaconda that has swallowed a peccary will perhaps lie contentedly twined in the exposed roots of a lignum vitae tree for the next three months. During this period the only sign of life will be the occasional flicking out of its tongue to sample the surrounding air. Captive specimens have been known to fast for better than two years before showing an active interest in eating when food was presented.

This ability to conserve food is common with all reptiles —lizards, alligators, turtles. I once had a baby alligator that I caught in early spring and kept in an aquarium. During the summer it became quite a pet and ate a wide variety of foods ranging from minnows and frogs to chunks of ground beef. Then, with the first cool days of fall it began to refuse food in any form, even though I would pry its jaws apart and place hamburger meat on its tongue.

After a six-month period of total fasting it grew thin and looked more like a skinny lizard than a baby alligator. With the return of spring, however, it suddenly became active and hungrily gobbled up every scrap of meat I dropped into the tank.

The art of photography, in both still pictures and movies, has become so much a part of the modern world that we find ourselves increasingly willing to place absolute faith in

the validity of film purported to be of a documentary nature.
Some years ago a popular animal collector exhibited a length
of film that should lend impetus to the old admonishment
that the cautious should believe nothing of what he hears
and only half of what he sees.

In the movie, which was exhibited worldwide, there were
a number of spine-tingling sequences showing the shooting
of a Bengal tiger, the capture of a rogue elephant, a battle
with a crocodile, and the charge of a rhino. During the
calmer moments the animal collector was shown with his
helpers placing a sixty-pound pig in a small bamboo cage.
The next morning there was great excitement in the camp
when the star of the show and his camera crew "discovered"
that a python had slipped into the compound and into the
bamboo cage. Supposedly, the reptile had swallowed the pig
and, with the bulk of the animal inside of it, had in effect
captured itself because it could not squeeze out through the
bars of the cage. It made an interesting film sequence for
those who knew little or nothing about snakes, but was
viewed with amusement by the herpetologist. In order to
capture itself in a manner such as was depicted in the film
the python would have had to stick its head and neck
through the cage bars and immediately commence to swallow the pig. The producers failed to explain how the python
was able to kill the pig, since the cage was not large enough
to accommodate both animal and snake at the same time.
The movie was apparently highly successful, however, and
if credulity was strained to the breaking point, one could
only shrug, remembering Hollywood's reputation for main-
taining a high regard for truth and using it sparingly.

In Central and South America many natives believe firmly
that boa constrictors and anacondas are responsible for the
death and disappearance of many cattle. It is, of course, entirely possible for a thirty-foot anaconda weighing nearly six

hundred pounds to kill and swallow a calf, and there can be no doubt that this occurs at times when a thirsty calf wanders along a pond or stream where an anaconda is resting in the weed-choked shallows. The snake would sense the approach of the small animal, and action would be swift. With the neck drawn back in a lateral loop and the sensitive tongue sampling the air time after time, the lidless eyes would stare unblinkingly at the approaching calf. When within range, the anaconda would strike and the jaws would slap shut like a bear trap on the calf's leg.

For the next few minutes the jungle air would be filled with the bawling of the terrified victim, and there would be a great commotion in the shallow water. Then, as the snake brought its powerful constrictive muscles into play, the cries from the calf would cease and so would its struggles. The snake would maintain its stranglehold until all signs of life had vanished and then for the next few hours patiently go about the laborious task of swallowing a meal that might possibly sustain it for the next three months.

That a very large snake occasionally swallows a small calf is understandable and natural. The cattle-stealing belief, however, goes deeper in the tropical countries of the Americas, and even reasonably intelligent people are firmly convinced that the giant constrictors make a practice of killing cattle for the sheer joy of killing.

With the exception of man, there are few creatures in nature that kill only for the excitement of the chase. The common weasel is probably one exception, for it has been known to slip into a hennery and wantonly kill as many as two dozen chickens while devouring only a small portion of one or two. Many domesticated dogs and cats will frequently exhibit exceptional zeal in their quest for rats and mice, which they generally disdain to eat after making the kill. In this case man seldom finds fault with his pets, and the dogs and cats are shrewd enough to know they are doing something to please their masters, who will reward the deeds with a more appetizing bill of fare.

It is entirely possible that a full-grown cow or bull might accidentally stumble onto a drowsing boa constrictor or anaconda. In such case the snake would immediately take defensive action and strike out at the animal and even throw its coils around the neck. But after the animal had been strangled to death the snake would disentangle itself and glide off into the brush. True, it killed the cow, but it did so only because it had been surprised and feared for its life.

One of the most frequently asked questions is whether large snakes occasionally devour human beings. There is no authenticated case, but there are dependable records of attacks on people by large constrictors from both the eastern and western hemisphere. Primitive tribes in both hemispheres credit the giant snakes with devouring a percentage of their numbers annually. The Seminole Indians of the Florida Everglades even believe that the harmless indigo snake grows to such proportions that it poses a menace to their children. The youngsters are admonished not to stray too far from the chickees in the belief that they may be caught and swallowed by an indigo snake. This fear is, of course, unfounded since there is no snake native to the United States that is large enough to swallow any child old enough to walk or even crawl.

The indigo snake, however, is one of the three longest snakes in the United States. It is reported to reach a length of ten feet, but the best reliable record is set at eight feet seven and one-half inches. Topping the indigo by only four and one-half inches is the bull snake, which is widely distributed through the central states. Its greatest reliable length thus far reported is nine feet. The title for length might eventually go to the Florida coachwhip, since one was found that measured eight and one half feet with an undetermined length of the tail missing.

Keepers and workmen in large zoos are careful never to enter a cage containing large constrictors unless there is adequate human help immediately available. There are few if any pythons or boas in captivity today that could actually swallow the average-size man, but there are plenty that could squeeze the life out of him, and such an accident did occur on March 17, 1961, to the owner of a Florida zoo.

Albert Henley owned a tourist attraction called Jungleland located just south of Tampa on U. S. Highway 41. All of the particulars concerning Henley's death are not known because he was working alone at the time. Extensive investigation by police and herpetologists, as well as examination of the autopsy report, indicates that shortly after breakfast Henley entered the compound and began working with his animals. There were many to be fed and watered and cages to be cleaned as part of the daily chores.

Sometime during the morning Henley apparently decided to move his twenty-one-foot reticulated python from one cage to another. He was an experienced snake handler, and as such it is surprising that he undertook the task without first making sure there was assistance nearby. His failure to do this cost him his life.

When Henley had not returned from the animal compound by noon his wife went to look for him. She found her husband's body lying at the base of a cabbage palm, and overhead in the fronds of the tree was the giant python.

The autopsy report did not disclose any broken bones in Henley's body, but it did determine that he had died of suffocation. Incised wounds suggested that the snake had broken loose from the man's grip and clamped its jaws around the wrist. Even at that point Henley may not have been aware of the seriousness of his predicament, because no one heard him call for help.

Familiar as he was with snakes he quite likely felt that he would be able to regain control of the python. But as man and snake struggled, the creature must have slipped a couple of its powerful coils around Henley's chest. It is speculated that another coil found its way around his head, shutting off the air to his nose and mouth.

By this time Henley no doubt recognized the danger, but it was too late. Unable to call for help and pressed down by the weight of the 210-pound snake he collapsed beneath the palm tree. How long the snake exerted its constricting pressure can only be guesswork. It may have been only minutes or over an hour.

There was no indication that the python had attempted to swallow Henley after killing him. This is not surprising, for any of several reasons. The width of a man's shoulders would present a problem for even a large snake such as this. Also, captive snakes, large ones in particular, are reluctant to eat even under ideal conditions. The unnatural surroundings with the smells of nearby highway traffic doubtless urged the python to concentrate only on making good its escape. Its refuge in the palm crown was just a temporary stopping place which it would have probably soon deserted had it not been recaptured.

There is no place for carelessness when handling wild animals of any kind, and this is particularly true where large or dangerous snakes are concerned. I have inadvertently proven this to myself on several occasions. One instance took place a few years ago when I was writing a series of articles about wildlife found in the American tropics. I wanted to get some good photographs to illustrate a piece I was working on about boa constrictors, and the owner of a small Florida zoo agreed to loan me one of the boas he had just received in a shipment from Central America.

Beyond the zoo was a stretch of woods, and I decided to carry the eleven-foot boa back into the trees to get a more realistic backdrop than could be set up in a cage. As she frequently does, my wife went along to handle the cameras.

For the first few minutes after we reached a sunlit spot everything went well. I positioned the boa on a low-hanging branch, and in less than an hour we had gotten several good shots. I was preparing to put the snake back into the canvas carrying bag when Dorothy suggested I pose with it held in front of me so that the relative size could be shown.

The midmorning sun had become increasingly warm, and I had grown weary with moving the fifty-pound snake from one spot to another. The snake, too, was feeling the effects of the heat and was becoming more recalcitrant with each passing minute. I was relieved when Dorothy gave me the signal that she had gotten the picture she wanted. As I started toward the canvas bag I must have inadvertently relaxed my grip on the snake's neck because its head slipped out of my grasp, and its jaws snapped shut on the cuff of my trousers. Feeling lucky that his teeth had not buried in my ankle, I quickly resolved to exercise more caution. The only trouble was that while I was concentrating on being careful not to permit a second bite I momentarily overlooked the snake's body and carelessly hefted the bulk up onto my left shoulder while I clutched its neck in the fingers of my right hand. Suddenly, I felt the snake's tail slipping around my waist, and before I could pull it free the boa managed to get nearly two full coils around the lower part of my chest. Instantly, it began to exert all of the pressure it could muster in

its body, and as the coils drew tighter I found it increasingly
difficult to take a deep breath.

Standing there in the sunshine I looked into the vacant
and lidless eyes of the boa constrictor while I fumbled
around with my left hand until my fingers closed around the
tip of its tail. As hard as I strained, however, I found I could
unwind only part of a coil, and it quickly became evident
that I needed help.

Dorothy was so preoccupied with putting away her photographic equipment that she had not paid any attention to me
until I began to waddle toward her. For a moment she
looked at me with a mixed expression of amusement and
concern on her face. But when I told her to grab the snake
by the tail and unwind it, all traces of mirth faded. During
our married life there has frequently been one or more
serpent boarders in cages in the basement or garage, and over
the years she overcame her natural aversion to being near
snakes, but she stoutly refused to handle any of them, large
or small, harmless or poisonous. I wondered now how she
would react and I wondered, too, how much longer I could
hold on. The fingers of my right hand were beginning to
ache from the pressure I was exerting on the snake's neck,
and the constriction of the coils around my body was becoming increasingly uncomfortable.

Much to my surprise and relief, Dorothy walked over to
where I was standing and calmly grasped the snake's tail with
both hands, and while I revolved in a slow-motion pirouette
she held fast and backed away. When I was free of the coils I
told her to drop the tail, and at the same instant I thrust the
head away from me.

The boa constrictor hit the ground as a writhing pile of
coils, and a moment later I had guided it back into the canvas carrying bag with my snake stick. While I secured the
bag with a length of cord Dorothy folded her camera case,

and we made our way to the compound. She had not hesitated to take hold of the snake a few minutes before, but now I noticed that she kept wiping first one hand and then the other along the side of her skirt, as if she had just been forced to shake hands with someone unclean.

2

ANATOMY

A few hundred million years ago a fish with a very long body swam up from the depths and floundered along over a tidal flat. It found no food to its liking and the sun was too hot, so the long fish left the mud flat and returned to the sea. There it remained content to swim about and feed and breed and reproduce in the manner of all fish for many more millions of years. Then, about a hundred million years ago, somewhere in the Cretaceous period, the long fish once again began to prowl about in the torpid shallows, and at times it would rest with its body partly out of the water.

Fins that had for so long been used for swimming, gradually became more useful as arms and legs, and the long fish began to drag and *walk* its body across the ooze of his early swamp. No change in animal anatomy happens overnight. Doubtlessly many more millions of years passed before the fins changed into legs, but when they did an enormously elongated lizard began to move about the land in an ungainly fashion. The long fish had become a snake with legs.

It is something of a wonder that the snake managed to survive after it left the sea, for it was certainly one of the most poorly equipped of all the early reptiles. All about it were dinosaurs, both large and small, and most of them were far better suited for that early life. The snake must have felt exceedingly underprivileged as it watched the fifty-ton brachiosaur contentedly munching on the lush vegetation, or the twenty-foot-tall *Tyrannosaurus rex* thundering along over a hillside in pursuit of some prey. In the air above it were the pterodactyls and other flying reptiles like the rhamphorhynchid that sailed along on outstretched wings. Almost all of the creatures were either too large to worry about attack or powerful enough to ward it off if it came. Those that were neither were generally so fleet-footed that they could outrun their adversaries. Then, too, there were others such as the *Paleoscincus* and *Styracosaurus* that depended upon their elaborate armor to protect them.

The early snake had neither size nor speed nor armor, and to make matters worse its legs were so small as to be more of a hindrance than a help when it came to locomotion. In that time when the snake was casting about for a new way to travel out of harm's way or in pursuit of his prey, it learned that by twisting its long body in a series of "S" shapes it could slither faster than it could run. It found that it could thrust its head and neck forward while pushing against the remainder of its body and then pull the tail section up close to the neck. The first attempts must have been clumsy and faltering, but it was better than walking.

Although she is slow about it, nature is generally obliging when one of her creatures discovers it no longer has a need for one of the appendages with which it has been blessed. Gradually that part that is no longer in use becomes smaller or inoperative and finally vanishes. The common mole that spends most of its life burrowing along in the darkness of underground is a good present-day example. The mole ceased to use its eyes, and nature took away its sight. The same is true of certain cave-dwelling fish that live only in the total darkness of subterranean rivers. When the snake finally perfected the art of crawling, or more properly gliding, along over the ground the legs began to vanish. Rudimentary traces of at least the hind legs are still to be found by careful dissection of some modern snakes.

To improve his twisting mode of travel, the snake began to employ the use of the scalelike belly shields that had come with it from the sea. Each shield on the underside of the body is controlled independently by muscles extending from nearly three hundred ribs. Working in unison like a row of falling dominoes, these scales press against any minute irregularity on the ground, and as they contract the snake is shoved forward.

Except for the withdrawal of the anterior coil, no snake can move backward. If it wishes to retreat it is obliged to reverse its direction.

The speed at which a snake can travel is often debated. No definite track records have been set, and the question will in all probability forever remain in doubt. Folklore of Africa has it that the deadly mamba can overtake a galloping horse and even a speeding automobile. This, is, of course, pure nonsense. Still, naturalists who have spent many hours in the field are repeatedly confounded by the speed some snakes occasionally exhibit.

There are conditions when a snake can double and even triple a man's running speed. In high grass, tangled underbrush, or over boulder-strewn ground the snake is in its own element and can easily outdistance a man stumbling along across such unfamiliar terrain. On level ground, however, few snakes could overtake a man walking along at a fast clip.

The snake was already well established on earth when man first put in his appearance. Gone by then were the giant dinosaurs and the huge flying lizards. When Adam and Eve stood alone in their Eden they saw trees and flowers and wildlife much as we see them today. They also saw the snake, and fossil remains prove that it has found no need to make any additional changes in its anatomy in the time it has been on earth with man.

Many millions of years before man appeared on earth, however, the snake went through one of the most startling evolutionary changes that any animal has ever experienced. It concerned its teeth and probably took place near the close of the Cretaceous period when the giant reptiles were coming to the end of their reign and mammals were assuming command.

After it left the sea the snake, which had always been carnivorous, now depended upon its strength, speed, and jaws to capture living land animals that appealed to its taste. In the very early times it was probably content to make a meal off any insect that happened along. But it seldom went hungry, because those early bugs were plentiful, and some, relatives of today's cockroaches, were nearly a foot in length, while there were dragon flys with a wingspread of nearly three feet. Still, they were simply insects, and a snake had only to catch one of them with its sharp recurved teeth and hold it until it stopped struggling; then the reptile could swallow at its leisure. With the appearance of mammals the snake found it could capture and swallow some of these creatures.

All went well for a while with the snake. It found plenty of insects and small mammals. Perhaps some thirty million years ago, however, while the snake was gliding about the land it met its first real adversary, and oddly enough, it came in the form of a bird. Paleontologists who have examined the fossils say this early bird, called the *Phororhacos*, stood nearly six feet tall. Its stubby wings and great body bulk made it flightless, and there is evidence that snakes formed an important part of its diet.

To escape the *Phororhacos* and other predatory birds and mammals, most snakes scurried off into the dense swamps and tangled brambles, but a few stood their ground and refused to be intimidated. In doing so a strange anatomical development began to take place. Two of the snake's teeth changed into hollow fangs that could inject a deadly venom into the bloodstream of any of their mammalian and avian adversaries.

At this point in ophidian evolution there arises one of the most baffling questions in all of nature. Why did only a very few types of snakes develop this highly specialized method of killing by poison while the vast majority continued to depend only upon their jaws and body strength? No one knows the answer and it is just another of the many secrets that nature holds.

In general terms snake fangs are divided into fixed and movable groups. There are also two types of venom, hemotoxic, which attacks the blood, and neurotoxic, which attacks the nerve cells.

The term "snakebite" is used loosely thoroughout the world, but in the true sense it applies only to such snakes as the cobras, corals, and others with fixed fangs. In these snakes, the method of injecting poison is actually a *bite*. They clamp their jaws onto their victim and sink their teeth and fangs into the flesh. As the pressure of the jaws is increased, venom is expelled.

The movable fangs of the vipers, such as the rattlesnakes, are much larger by comparison than fixed fangs, and the mechanics of the bite are considerably more complicated. The movable fangs are situated in the anterior part of the upper jaw, and when not in use they lie encased in sheaths in the roof of the mouth. When these snakes open their mouths under normal conditions the fangs are not visible. They are exposed only in the brief interval that the snake is striking. With the use of high-speed photography we can get a clear picture of what happens when a viper strikes; but photography can give only the external picture, and to comprehend fully what happens when a snake strikes, the entire venom apparatus must be examined.

The alarmed snake draws part of its body into a tight mass with about one-third of the neck and forward portion retracted in an S-shaped coil. When the target is within range, the snake projects this coil forward. As it moves, the mouth is opened wide so that the two jaws are about as far apart as the thumb and forefinger on a splayed human hand. As the laterally formed coil darts out, the fangs are erected. If the strike is perfect they are driven into the flesh of the victim.

At the instant of contact the base of the hollow fangs are pressed back against the roof of the snake's mouth, and simultaneously powerful muscles surrounding the poison sacs on either side of the head contract, automatically sending the venom through the fangs in exactly the same manner as a hypodermic needle. The head and neck are immediately withdrawn to the original defensive pose. If molested further the snake will strike again and again. In contrast, the fixed fang snakes such as the cobras, corals, and mambas will often hang onto their victims and "chew" until beaten off.

At this point it should be noted that snakes do not have to be coiled before striking. I had this graphically proven to me some years ago on a summer hiking trip. My two companions and I had paused for a midmorning snack on a rustic log bridge that spanned a small mountain stream. While we were sipping lukewarm water from our canteens and munching dried apricots I chanced to spot a copperhead sunning itself on a rock below. Taking aim with my .22 rifle I squeezed off

a shot and watched the snake writhe in what I supposed to
be a death struggle.

Setting my gun aside, I made my way down to the creek
bottom and picked up the still-convulsing snake by the tail.
Returning to the bridge I was holding it at arm's length in
my right hand and pointing with my left to the hole the bullet had made. Suddenly the injured snake lashed out and
struck me on the left forearm.

Dropping the copperhead I stared at my arm. There was
a tiny spot of blood, and a wheal of white flesh, similar to
that caused by an insect sting, was beginning to form. Only
one of the snake's fangs had made contact, and there was a
burning sensation near the wound while a dull ache centered
around my elbow.

My two friends and I had been Boy Scouts for a number
of years. We each *knew* what had to be done in the case of a
poisonous snakebite. I knotted a handkerchief above my
elbow in the form of a tourniquet and opened my pocketknife. The blade was sharp, and gritting my teeth, I made a
small incision over the fang puncture. I had always imagined
the treatment of snakebite would be a coldly calculated operation, but I had not reckoned with the fact that I would be
cutting into my own flesh with a knife I had previously used
only for such chores as sharpening tent stakes and cleaning
fish. I think the task of making that incision on my arm
brought about an anguish greater than the fear of the snakebite itself.

As the blood began to flow from the wound I put the knife
aside and began to suck out the venom—or, at least, I con-
soled myself in the belief I was getting it out. Half an hour
later and after much spitting and gagging, I decided to quit
sucking, and my friends made me as comfortable as they
could in the shade of a maple tree while they went about the
business of setting up camp.

Most of the afternoon was spent in a sort of stupor, and I had a seemingly unquenchable thirst. My arm swelled, my head ached, and I felt weak when I attempted to stand. We discussed the idea of getting to medical help, but our map showed the nearest road to be nearly five miles away over rugged mountain terrain. It was much too far for my companions to carry me on an improvised stretcher, and I was convinced that I could not walk the distance. The result was that we stayed put, and by the following morning my headache was gone and the swelling in my arm was considerably reduced. The wound made with my pocketknife remained sore and showed signs of infection for nearly a week.

Reflecting on that case of snakebite, I wonder just how many things I did that did not need to be done. I wonder, too, what I would do if confronted with a similar situation today. At that time I was under the impression that the venom of a copperhead was equally as dangerous as that from a rattlesnake or a water moccasin. Later investigation has proved that the toxic properties of copperhead venom is the lowest of all of the pit vipers. Considering the fact that only one of the fangs entered my flesh, and that not very deeply, I suspect I would have fared better if I had done nothing more than daub the fang puncture with iodine and had taken it easy for the rest of the day.

The wonder of it is that I did not do myself serious harm with my pocketknife, which could not have been very sterile. Also, the careless and prolonged use of the tourniquet could have caused a case of gangrene. I strongly suspect that my recovery was occasioned as much by the hearty constitution of a teen-ager as by the first aid treatment.

While considering the toxicity of copperhead venom it is interesting to recall the story by the late Albert Payson Terhune, who wrote so extensively about his Sunnybank collies. In his book *Lad: A Dog,* Terhune relates the story of his dog, who deliberately thrust himself between a small child and a coiled copperhead. The child was unharmed, but the brave dog was struck twice on the muzzle by the snake before he was able to kill it.

The dog then slipped away and was not seen for nearly a week. When he did return his head was badly swollen and his entire body was matted with a thick coat of mud. Terhune's conclusion was that his canine hero had followed an instinct far older than the practice of medicine and had partially submerged himself in the ooze of a secluded New Jersey marsh until the effects of the venom had dissipated.

In another case, I saw a dog bitten full in the face by a large copperhead in King William County, Virginia. This dog, too, vanished in the woods and was not seen for four days. At that time she stumbled back into the barnyard with a greatly swollen head. Like Terhune's Lad, she had elected to wait out her illness away from her human friends. In both cases, the dogs obviously spent a period of suffering, but the toxicity of the venom had not been strong enough to cause death. In either incident, had the snake been a rattlesnake or a water moccasin the dogs would hardly have recovered. The copperhead has occasionally been responsible for human deaths in North America, but these are so few and far between as to make one wonder if this snake should be rated as one of the deadly poisonous ones.

Another important consideration in the strike of a snake is the extent of its reach. No snake in North America can exceed half the length of its body in a strike. As a rule the distance is something less than one-third the total length. An exception to this rule is when a snake is striking at a downhill target. Then the momentum of the snake's body may carry the head to a greater distance. A snake striking from the top of a rock or log may actually seem to jump, but there are no jumping snakes in North America.

Snake venom is still a mystery to science and has yet defied a complete chemical analysis. What facts there are show it to contain largely a protein base. It is a clear liquid, slightly yellow in color, and is tasteless and odorless. The normal human could, if he wanted to, drink it without suffering any ill effects. Such a beverage, however, would not be recommended for anyone who had just had a tooth pulled or people with bleeding stomach ulcers. In such cases it is possible that some of the venom might be absorbed into the bloodstream.

When venom is dried it turns into crystals, and in this state it may be kept for years without deterioration. When these crystals are mixed with water and injected into test animals the potency is just as strong as if the venom had come directly from the fangs of a living snake. It is interesting to note that if venom is boiled for a short while it becomes harmless. Also its poison weakens rapidly after a snake is killed.

Just as baffling to science as the chemical analysis is the method by which a snake manufactures its poison. The potency varies with different types of snakes and even with snakes of the same species and size. Venom from some freshly caught snakes appears to be more virulent than that extracted after the snake has been in captivity for a long period of time. Again, there seems to be no change in the potency of other snakes' poison no matter how long it is kept. It has been suggested that the wide variation in the toxicity of venom may have a direct relation to certain items of diet which a snake eats at times and not at others.

The venomous fangs of a snake are highly efficient weapons, perhaps unrivaled in all of nature, when it comes to collecting food. Most carnivorous animals, including man, often cause great suffering to the creature out of which they plan to make a meal. A pack of wolves will pull down a caribou and tear at its intestines while the doomed animal attempts to drag itself along the ground. Some birds are just as cruel. I once observed a bluejay feasting on the living flesh of a nest of fledgling sparrows. Most people would find their steaks and chops less appetizing if they could see the methods of killing employed at modern abattoirs.

The poisonous snake is almost a humanitarian in the slaughter of food it must have to survive. Watch a rattlesnake kill a rat, and then compare the clean efficiency of the job with the methods employed by a cat or terrier when a rodent is the target of the hunt.

The rattlesnake invades a barn at twilight. Its highly sensitive olfactory nerves have suggested that the barn with its bins of grain and bales of hay constitutes a natural habitat for creatures like rats and mice. They represent food to it, and it is hungry. As the snake moves across the floor of the barn its string of rattles is held high, but they are silent as it takes up station near a corn crib. It draws its body into a pile of loose coils, and for perhaps an hour it waits almost motionless in the strange surroundings. Suddenly, it becomes alert. The snake lifts its head and its tongue darts out; sampling the air. It cannot see, but it knows a rat is approaching.

The rodent has just left the chicken house where it killed and ate part of a young hen. Now it is on its way back to the catacomb beneath the barn floor where it plans to sleep for a few hours. The snake is fully awake, and every nerve in its body is tense. The head draws back, and the neck is in a lateral coil. There is no sound from the string of rattles because the snake is hunting, and it uses its rattles only to warn away an enemy that cannot serve as food. The rat darts across the floor and suddenly there is a swift movement beside it. The impact of the snake's fangs knocks the rat off its feet, but a second later it has recovered and is running. Twenty feet away the victim slows down and its legs begin to falter as the lethal dose of venom spreads through its body. The snake makes no effort to hurry after the rat, because the attacker knows its aim was true. When the poison has done its work the serpent's sensitive nose will guide it to the dying rat.

The process of swallowing for a snake is a complicated operation quite unlike anything else in nature. All snakes have teeth, but in no case are they suited for mastication. Whatever the snake eats must be swallowed whole. The rattler that has just killed the rat has a neck circumference of about four inches while the rat is as big around as a baseball. Logic suggests the snake had better abandon its kill and go in search of something smaller, but the snake is not the least concerned. It knows exactly what it is going to do and it does not waste time. When it locates the rat's head the snake's jaws open and fit themselves around it and at that moment powerful muscles, aided by the recurved teeth, begin to pull the rodent down into the snake's gullet. The jaw bones are hinged at the front and back by elastic ligaments, and as the larger part of the rat enters the mouth these bones spread apart until at the maximum extension the snake's head is quite distorted.

Once past the mouth, the rat is drawn along through the throat by muscles. When it reaches the stomach strong acids begin the digestive process. During the period of digestion the snake prefers to lie practically motionless in some hiding place. Although it may appear to be asleep it is constantly on the alert and will strike if molested by an intruder. On the other hand, dozens of other rats may pass within easy reach and not be bothered. Only when it has rested and fully digested its meal will it begin to prowl again for food.

All snakes are cold-blooded, and the temperature of the air around them has a direct bearing on the amount of activity they exhibit. In the temperate zone of North America they are active night and day during the summer months, but when the first chill of autumn comes they begin to seek out places of hibernation. In Canada and the northern section of the United States no snake is ever found abroad in winter. In the southern states, however, they may hibernate for short periods and come out as soon as there is a warming trend. They may, in fact, hibernate several times during the same winter. No tropical snake ever hibernates during its life.

During the summer months snakes range over the countryside, resting in the heat of the day in the shade of a boulder or beside a fallen tree. Temperatures between seventy and ninety degrees Fahrenheit are most to their liking. When the heat goes over the hundred-degree mark they become less active and often lapse into a temporary state of aestivation, seeking shelter in the coolest spot they can find. Below seventy degrees they again begin to slow down. When the night temperature drops below fifty degrees the snake is virtually motionless, but it is not harmed by these brief extremes. One exception to this is that if a snake is trapped in a place where it can find no shade the direct rays of the summer sun will kill it in short order.

But snakes are seldom caught off base. From birth they live in a somewhat restricted area, and during the warm months they cover their territory and learn it as thoroughly as a fox knows its own private stretch of woods, or a tough old tom cat acquaints itself with the few square blocks that comprise its kingdom. There are always exceptions. Forest fires will occasionally drive snakes far away from their natural range, and to a lesser extent local floods will do the same; but for the most part, snakes tend to spend their lives in the general area in which they are born.

When fall comes several snakes and sometimes even hundreds of them will choose the same place of hibernation and return there year after year to pass the winter. While not normally gregarious, they tend to congregate when it comes time to hibernate. Frequently several different species will share the same habitat in complete harmony.

Some snakes are born alive while others hatch from eggs. In North America all poisonous snakes with the exception of the coral are viviparous. Life begins, for example, for a copperhead sometime in late summer when the gravid female slides through a dense stand of tall grass and rests beside a rotting log. She is ready to give birth, and before two hours have passed she has let half a dozen or more pencil-size little copperheads escape her body. The mother snake does not care what her offspring look like, nor for that matter does she care what happens to them. All that nature has commanded her to do is to find a reasonably safe place in which to produce her young. That done, what happens to the youngsters is up to them and nature.

Shortly after birth the young snakes will slide off through the grass, and with a little luck they will stand a fair chance of growing into adults. Sometime, when the female is still resting, the young will remain near her for a day or so, but she offers them no help in finding food.

For a while the little copperhead hides beneath the shelter of a leaf or in a hollow spot under a rock. It flexes its tiny jaws, and for the first time the threadlike forked tongue slips out of the sheath in the bottom jaw and tastes the air. It sees something move and instinct says it is food. The head darts out and the jaws close around a small grasshopper. Gradually the insect is swallowed and the copperhead has eaten its first meal. There will be many more grasshoppers, crickets, and grubs to eat during what is left of the summer, and the snake will nearly double in size. When the cool nights of fall begin the little copperhead will search about for a place in which to hibernate, and this first winter will be spent alone, perhaps under a decaying stump or deep in some hole in the ground which it happens to find.

If it has chosen the spot well and does not freeze during the winter it will awaken with the coming of the spring rains. As the sun begins to warm the earth it will leave its retreat and begin to hunt for more of the same insects it was eating shortly after it was born. Eventually, it will happen upon a nest of newly born field mice. The juvenile copperhead will ponder the tiny rodents for a moment and then decide that here is a feast to its liking. Before that second summer is over the young snake has learned two important facts. One is that it would rather eat warm-blooded creatures instead of insects, and the other is that the tiny fangs in the roof of its mouth will stun mice and other little animals that wander close to it. Its fangs and poison sacs were functional from the first day it was born, but it takes it a while to learn to use them in catching something to eat.

In the closing days of the second summer the young copperhead finds itself moving inexorably in a general uphill direction. It does not know why it must head this way, but some force is urging it along. The nights are becoming cold again, but this time the snake does not search for a stump or hole in the ground. During the day it moves about and spends the nights in the shelter of rocks that have been warmed by the sun.

The leaves of the beeches and maples have turned yellow and red, and acorns are falling from the oaks. The snake has eaten well during the summer and grown fat. Time after time it passes up animals that it could capture because it is no longer interested in feeding.

Eventually the copperhead reaches a mass of shattered rocks that had once been the sheer face of a cliff. An earthquake ages ago caused it to tumble and slide, and with the passage of time the earth and the forest covered it and changed it into an irregular stretch on the hillside. Somewhere in this area the copperhead knows it will find the place where it will spend the winter. It is the home of its parents and has been the home of its ancestors for thousands of generations. It is the focal point or gathering place for all of the copperheads and rattlesnakes in the area, and they will share it peacefully with many nonpoisonous snakes that are also converging on the hillside.

During its lifetime the average snake ranges over ten to fifteen square miles that surround the spot where it spends the winter. One year it may travel in a northerly direction for about two miles. The next year it may go approximately the same distance in another direction. Two miles is the radius of its circle, and if the geometric formula of πR^2 is applied, it can be seen that a snake's range is a little over half the size of Manhattan.

Naturally, no snake's range is ever in a perfect circle. It may be kidney-shaped or in the form of an hourglass or a stretch of ground that twists first one way and then another. Natural and man-made barriers are generally the factors that determine the boundaries. A heavily traveled highway may form a straight line on one side, and a swift and twisting river may cut off the other side.

If a snake's range is to be perfect it must have three essential factors besides the rocky ledge or other place that provides suitable hibernation. It must have an ample supply of water in the form of springs, ponds, and creeks. It must have adequate shelter to hide the snake from its enemies and to protect it from the sun. The third requirement is an ample supply of food. It is the type of specialized range that causes certain types of snakes to associate with some entirely different species while still others are totally absent. For example, the water snakes with a diet consisting primarily of frogs, fish, and other aquatic animals would not consider making their home on a hillside where birds and mammals would be the chief game.

When the summer is finally gone the copperhead and other types of snakes begin to crawl into the den or cave where they will spend the winter. When the cold weather comes they gradually sink into the torpor of hibernation. For the next half year they will remain virtually motionless. Respiration comes almost to a standstill as does the beating of the heart. If in the dead of winter a human intruder happened to enter the cave he would be able to pick up the sleeping snakes and move them about from one place to another as if they were nothing more than potted plants.

Late in March or early April the days grow longer and the north-bound sun becomes warmer. Heavy rains wash the hillside free of the last patches of snow and balmy breezes, scented with wild flowers and fresh grass, will waft down into the cave. First one snake and then another will begin to make almost imperceptible movements. The temperature inside the cave will rise only a few degrees—hardly more than it might have done half a dozen times during the winter in periods of unseasonable warmth—but the great time clock that governs all nature will set its silent alarm chiming, and the snakes will awaken from their long sleep. But there will be no headlong rush to leave the cave and begin another summer of hunting. At first they will make exploratory sorties to the ledge and stare out into the sunlight for a few hours near the middle of the day and then repair to their bedroom for another forty winks.

Eventually, after a week or two, the lure of the fresh, warm air will cause the snakes to desert the cave. It would be logical to assume, by human standards, that after awakening from such a long sleep the first thing the snake would think of would be looking around for something to eat. It will be remembered, however, that the snake's metabolism has been practically dormant during the winter, and it is hardly more hungry than it was when it began its hibernation.

Instead of hunger it is possessed with another basic urge of all animals, reproduction. This is one of the few times when snakes will show definite signs of attacking any creature that wanders near their den. I had this proven to me one spring morning on a North Carolina hillside some years ago.

The time was mid-April and spring was in full bloom across the land. I parked my car on the side of a little-used country road and looked down on a stream that spilled through the valley below. The chain of pools and fast-flowing rapids that I had been able to see from the road suggested that it might hold good fishing possibilities. I took my fly rod from the back seat, and before leaving the car I strapped my .22 target pistol around my waist.

For the most part the route down the hillside was a pleasant hike through the spring woods. About halfway down to the creek I came to a spot where the ground dropped abruptly. I paused at the edge of the tiny cliff and looked down. Perhaps six feet below and right at the base of the ledge was a massive flat boulder surrounded by a sea of tangled vines and low bushes. My first impulse was to climb down the ledge to the boulder. Reconsidering, I decided to jump the intervening space. It is probably very well that I chose the latter course.

I jumped and landed on a flat rock with a jolt, and at the same instant I heard the sound of a rattlesnake buzzing, and then there was another. Before I could get my bearings the air seemed to be full of the sound of singing rattles. Turning around quickly I faced the low cliff. At that moment I saw more snakes than I have ever seen before or since outside the reptile house at a zoo, and most of them were rattlers and copperheads.

Seen from the front side the cliff was a series of layers of flat rocks with cracks between each layer that ranged from a foot to only a few inches. In front of each crevasse were ledges like miniature terraces on an apartment building and each of these terraces were literally covered with snakes. It seemed that most of the occupants of this communal dwelling were banded rattlesnakes, and scattered among them were a number of copperheads with their distinctive saddle markings. Here and there I saw groups of three or four snakes packed tightly together, and I guessed most of them were males trying to win the favor of females. Perhaps if I had left things alone I would not have been bothered, but the sight of so many poisonous snakes close by urged me to take out my automatic and do a bit of shooting. My first target was a thick-bodied rattler near the top of the cliff. When my bullet hit it, it came thrashing and twisting down the side, dislodging several other snakes as it fell. At that point a dozen or more tumbled off the ledges and disappeared in the vine cover surrounding my boulder.

Immediately I regretted my action, because if I was to get off the rock and continue on toward the creek, I was going to have to wade through that grass, and I could see more and more snakes sliding down into it. Taking aim I shot another rattler, and just at that moment I saw a copperhead sliding up on the rock with me. It moved steadily toward me with its head and neck drawn back in a lateral loop. It was an easy target, but when two other snakes tried to come up on the rock with me I began to feel apprehensive about my position and the Pandora's box I had opened.

Common sense insisted that I was in no danger as long as I stayed on the rock, but the sight of so many snakes was unnerving. I jammed the pistol back into the holster, picked up my fly rod and leaped off the downhill side of the rock. The vines and bushes were knee deep and I bounded through them like a gazelle; expecting at any second to feel a stab of pain that would let me know I had been bitten. It did not happen, but I did not stop running until I was in a wide open spot. Needless to say, after leaving the creek I followed a wide and circuitous route on my way back to the car.

In most of North America, early spring, just after they emerge from hibernation, is the breeding season for snakes. And, except for their long winter's sleep, it is the only time they will have anything to do with others of their kind. Copulation is relatively simple and devoid of emotion so often displayed by other creatures of the animal kingdom. When she is ready for breeding the female begins to exude a scent designed to lure a male to her side. There is something like a form of courtship that lasts for a few minutes when the snakes do come together. The male slides along over the female's body while his tongue flicks in and out of his mouth. When the union is actually made it may last anywhere from a few minutes to well over an hour, after which they separate, each snake going its own way.

Many are the tales about snakes avenging the death of a mate. Such is just plain nonsense, but it is a superstition that probably will long be with us simply because it makes a good yarn. The fact is that no snake cares one whit about the fate of its mate. For that matter it cares nothing about what happens to its offspring, its siblings, or its parents. As with all superstitions, however, there is generally some tiny seed of truth that leads to the belief.

The story about the avenging mate quite likely began in some tropical country where poisonous snakes are abundant. A female cobra in India, for instance, might be killed in a tiny village while prowling about in someone's house. Later that day a male cobra enters the same house and bites the person responsible for the death of the first snake. To those who subscribe to the avenging superstition, this is an open and shut case proving beyond doubt that it is a dangerous thing to kill a snake if its mate is nearby. The true facts are that the male cobra was simply following the scent trail left by the female, and that he bit the householder means only that he was luckier or more alert than his intended mate. He would have bitten just the same if there had never been a female in the house.

Some snakes are oviparous while others are viviparous. In North America the coral is the only poisonous snake that lays eggs. All of the pit vipers—the rattlers, copperheads, and water moccasins—give birth to their young alive. In the majority of cases where oviparous snakes are concerned, the mother does not bother herself with the elaborate construction of nests such as are built by most birds. For that matter, even alligators and crocodiles do a far better job. The female snake looks around until she finds a spot that is fairly well drained and a place that offers good natural cover. Often this may be only a mass of rotting ferns or the debris of a decaying log. She may use her neck as a sort of shovel to scoop out a slight depression, and in this she deposits her eggs. When she has finished she will glide away with never a backward glance and not the slightest interest in whether the eggs hatch or are eaten the next day by a bird or some other predator. Such a careless attitude is not true where all reptiles are concerned. A female alligator, for example, builds a massive nest and then guards it zealously and often with ferocity during the time her clutch of eggs is incubating and even after the little alligators have hatched.

Viviparous mother snakes are not much more attentive than their egg-laying cousins. If unhurried they will occasionally remain in the vicinity where their brood is delivered for a day or so, but this is more to rest from her ordeal than any manifestation of maternal protectiveness.

Almost everyone who has spent much time wandering about in the outdoors has occasionally found a snake's skin. Sometimes it will be only a few inches long, and again it will measure several feet in length. Whatever the case, it will give a good idea of the size of the snake that left it, and if the scales are examined it is possible to tell what kind of snake it came from.

If the skin is in good condition it looks like a translucent plastic tube. All snakes shed their skins many times during their lives, and the shedding process is one way they differ from many other reptiles. Turtles and alligators, for instance, never shed. They grow slowly, and while parts of the epidermis break off from time to time, they never slip out of their old suit all at one time.

While totally unrelated, snakes are similar to crabs and other arthropods which must periodically cast off their old outer covering in order to grow. In a short summer, when spring is late and fall comes early, a snake may shed its skin only once. The following year summer may begin early and fall come late. If food is plentiful the same snake may cast off three and even four skins. In a typical year in temperate zones a snake will begin to find itself almost blind sometime in early summer because of the loosening of the skin about its head. It is as if a veil of gauze might be covering the lidless convex eyes, and at that time the snake seeks out some safe retreat while the shedding process continues. The skin around the head loosens first, and the reptile begins to scrub its head on stones and bushes to get the shedding started. When the skin around the jaws finally breaks, the snake starts to crawl until the loose skin catches on some obstruction. Then, inch by inch the reptile emerges, turning the skin wrong side out as it moves.

Just after shedding, a snake shows its brightest colors and truest markings. This may last for several days, but as time passes, the colors become dull and faded, and various environmental conditions may actually cause a normally colorful snake to become so drab and stained as to escape identification by a casual observer.

During its evolution the snake has become probably the most highly specialized of all vertebrates. What happened to the twin lungs, common to almost all creatures, is a good example of some of the changes a snake has made. When its body continued to grow in length, yet not get much bigger around, the snake's lungs underwent an extraordinary change. The double lung was discarded in favor of one very long one. Not that it was better or more effective, but simply that it fit better into the snake's tubular anatomy. Under the normal conditions with which a snake must cope, the single lung serves well. Its limited capacity for air storage, however, causes the snake to tire quickly. It can strike with lightning speed and glide swiftly across the ground in short sprints. If subjected to continuous exertion, the lung is incapable of providing the needed air, and the snake becomes exhausted.

The heart followed the pattern of the lung and became greatly elongated. The same is true of all of the other internal organs, from the gullet through the stomach to the intestines.

No snake has ears in the true sense of the word, certainly not external ears like a fox or a bat, nor even the disklike ears found on frogs, lizards, and certain other reptiles. It is logical to assume that a creature without ears would be as incapable of hearing as one without eyes would be unable to see. This, however, is not entirely so. Many snakes, especially those that live on the ground, seem to *hear* well, but the sound is felt rather than heard. Sound waves such as those produced by the footfalls of an approaching animal are transmitted through the earth and are picked up by sensitive nerves connected to the lower jaw bone and probably the entire underside of the body. It is like a delicate seismograph that detects the slightest vibrations in the earth and transmits them to the snake's brain. The interesting part about it is that by some strange method a snake's hearing apparatus is so sensitive and selective that it can detect the light footfalls of a small animal trotting along in a heavy downpour of rain or when wind is rustling leaves and shaking bushes.

It has long been an accepted belief that no snake is capable of sensing airborne sounds. Recent experiments, however, have produced evidence to the contrary, and further investigation may prove that at least some snakes can hear certain sounds. I once kept a pet black racer that I was convinced could hear a sharp whistle emitted near its cage.

A snake's forked tongue is believed by the uninformed to be some kind of stinger. This is not so. There is nothing about the tongue that is poisonous, nor is it in any way capable of producing injury. Instead, it is actually part of a highly sensitive olfactory system. When not in use the tongue lies encased in a sheath in the middle of the lower jaw. When some scent is detected through the nostrils and a snake wishes to investigate it further, the tongue is extended and picks up minute particles which are quickly transferred to sense organs in the roof of the mouth. Even the faintest whiff of smoke will cause a drowsing snake to become alert. It will lift its head and begin tasting the air with its tongue. If this gives warning of an approaching forest fire, the snake will begin to take evasive action.

3

MOST DANGEROUS

Each geographical region of the tropical and subtropical world has one or more snakes that stand out from all the rest because of their danger to human life. This is not always necessarily the snake with the most toxic venom, nor is it always the largest poisonous snake of a given region. In the United States the largest poisonous snake is the eastern diamondback (*Crotalus adamanteus*) with record specimens reaching nearly eight feet in length. The one responsible for the most deaths in this country, however, is the western diamondback (*Crotalus atrox*). The copperhead (*Agkistrodon contortrix*) has the distinction of being responsible for more bites than any other poisonous snake in the United States, but because of the relatively low toxicity of its venom, its bite is rarely fatal. Approximately a million and a half people die each year in the United States, and of this number only about fifty deaths are attributed to snakebite. In view of these figures it can be seen that snakebite does not constitute a serious menace in this country.

The picture is quite different in southeastern Asia where annually approximately thirty thousand people are killed by poisonous snakes. In this region the cobras are the real bad actors. Again, however, it is not the largest and most fearsome that accounts for the most deaths. The king cobra (*Ophiophagus hannah*) wears the undisputed crown for being the largest poisonous snake in the world. One specimen measured eighteen feet four inches in length, which is just two inches short of the record length for a boa constrictor. Despite its great size and abundance of venom, the king cobra is not the deadliest of snakes; more properly, it is not responsible for the greatest number of human deaths.

It is generally agreed among investigators that the Asiatic or hooded cobra (*Naja naja*) kills more people than any other species of snake in the world. Running a close second and third are the kraits and vipers. All three of these snakes have highly toxic venoms, and all inhabit areas of dense human population.

The most dreaded snakes in all of Africa are the mambas (*Dendraspis spp.*) of which there are four species, all indigenous to the Dark Continent. Far and away the worst of these is the black mamba (*Dendraspis polylepis*), which attains a length of fourteen feet.

The mamba is so generally feared throughout Africa that a host of fearful tales are told about it, and sometimes it is difficult to separate the fact from the fiction. The most popular of these stories concern the mamba's great speed. According to the lore it is absolutely useless for a man to attempt to outrun one of these snakes, and they have been reported to overtake and attack galloping horses and speeding automobiles. All of which is, of course, just so much nonsense, but believed by many people.

The mamba is a member of the Elapidae family and closely related to the cobras, with large fangs situated near the anterior of the mouth. Despite some of the ridiculous myths concerning its great speed, the mamba is a swift snake,

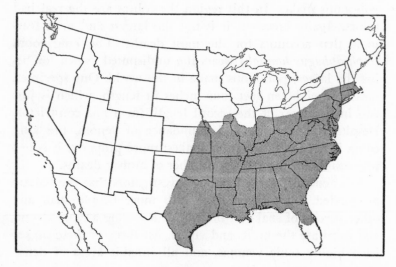

COPPERHEADS

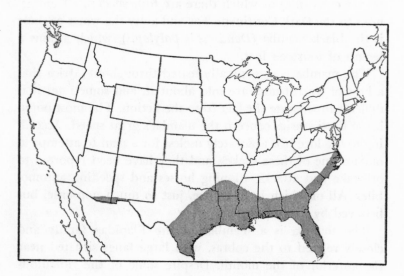

CORAL SNAKES

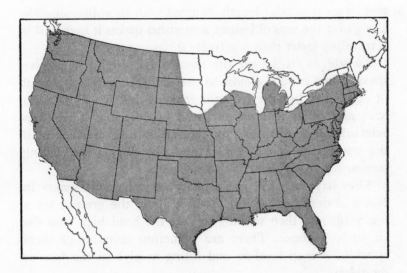

RATTLESNAKES

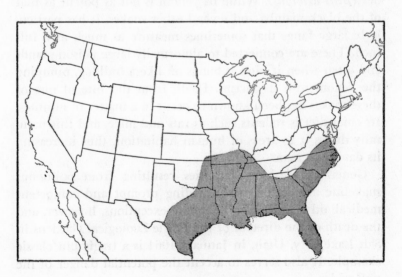

WATER MOCCASINS

and its great slender length, coupled with its ability to glide along over the tops of bushes, sometimes makes it look as if it is traveling faster than it actually is.

To add to its danger the mamba is a highly aggressive snake. Some experts choose to use the word *nervous* instead of aggressive, but the fact still remains that it will attack a man and often without apparent provocation. This characteristic often manifests itself to an even greater extent if the snake feels it is cornered and also during the mating season.

They have a habit, as do many nonvenomous snakes in North America, of gliding swiftly along the ground for a few yards and then pausing to rear the head high into the air to look about. There are numerous accounts of them attacking a man head-on and biting as high as the face or shoulders.

Another of Africa's most dangerous snakes is the puff adder (*Bitis arietans*). While its venom is not as potent as that of the black mamba and several other snakes, it has particularly large fangs that sometimes measure as much as a full inch. These are connected to abnormally large poison glands and often when it bites it hangs on like a bulldog, pumping the venom into its victim. Death from the bite of one of these snakes has been known to occur in a matter of minutes. Its chief diet is rodents such as rats and mice, and this naturally draws it to areas of human habitation, thus increasing its danger to man.

Generally speaking, fatalities resulting from poisonous snakebite are almost nil providing prompt and competent medical aid is available. There are exceptions, however, and the death of the director of the Hogle Zoological Gardens in Salt Lake City, Utah, in January 1964 is a tragic but classic example. It also serves to accent the potential danger of the puff adder.

On Saturday night, January 25, 1964, Gerald de Bary, director of the Gardens, was winding up the chore of cleaning the reptile cages. As part of the safety procedure, De Bary had decreed that the cages were not to be cleaned until all visitors had left the gardens. The time was approximately 10:30 P.M. when he opened the door of the puff adder cage. For some reason that De Bary was not able to explain, and which could not later be determined by physicians, the thirty-seven-year-old director suddenly experienced a moment of dizziness, and in an effort to avoid falling he threw up his left arm and clutched at the door frame. His hand missed its intended grip, however, and his arm was thrust into the puff adder's cage. Instantly, the snake struck, imbedding both fangs deeply into the underside of the forearm.

The pain caused by the snake's fangs entering his flesh snapped De Bary back to full consciousness, and he steadied himself and quickly closed the door, pausing long enough to see that it was securely locked.

There were two assistant keepers in the gardens at the time, and a call from De Bary brought both of them to his side. One of the men immediately placed an improvised tourniquet around the director's arm. The events that followed the placing of the tourniquet may or may not have been of vital importance, but they are worth relating.

Earlier that same evening De Bary had taken time to show one of his assistants where the supply of antivenin was stored in the refrigerator in the keeper's room. While being helped into this room De Bary apparently forgot about the antivenin that was practically within arm's reach, and he dispatched one of his assistants to the small animal hospital some distance away where an additional supply of serum was kept. In the confusion the assistant failed to bring a hypodermic syringe, and more time was lost while he was sent back after it. None of the three men remembered that everything they needed was in the refrigerator in the same room with them.

In the first few minutes after the accident another of De Bary's assistants had placed a call to the Salt Lake City police, explaining the nature of the accident and requesting an ambulance. The call was answered within five minutes, and a police reporter by the name of Art Kent arrived with the ambulance. Kent had knowledge of the type of injection that was needed, and under De Bary's instruction, he prepared the antivenin and gave the first injection. This was administered about twenty minutes after the puff adder had struck. Ten minutes later Dr. George D. Gross, who had also been summoned by telephone, arrived at the zoo. The following is the clinical report taken from his notes.

Upon arriving Dr. Gross noted that De Bary's left forearm was beginning to swell and the flesh was becoming discolored. He quickly had the zoo director transferred to the county hospital and administered an additional 10 cc. of antivenin en route in the police ambulance.

By the time De Bary reached the hospital he was beginning to complain of a tingling sensation in both hands, mild abdominal cramping, and a burning pain in his left arm and shoulder. The left arm was packed in ice.

During the remainder of the night additional serum was administered at half-hour intervals, and several shots were given to relieve pain. De Bary's temperature rose to 105 degrees, and he went in and out of shock. Breathing became increasingly difficult to the extent that oxygen was started by mask.

By eight o'clock the following morning his pulse was weak and rapid at two hundred beats per minute. In order to improve the action of the heart he was digitalized. An hour later Dr. Gross ordered a tracheotomy performed because of a swelling over the throat that promised to worsen.

By then there was massive edema of De Bary's left arm and the left side of his chest. Voiding of urine had become almost impossible and several attempts were made to use an artificial kidney, but each time it was begun De Bary lapsed into a state of shock. Except for times when his fever was exceptionally high or when he was in shock, the zoo director was well oriented and conversed freely with those around him.

At five thirty Monday morning, nearly thirty hours after being bitten by the puff adder, De Bary seemed to be holding his own fairly well, and Dr. Gross noted with satisfaction that vital signs were stable and there was a general improvement in his clinical condition. Although parts of his body, including his face, were seriously swollen due to a tremendous amount of serous fluid in the tissue spaces, De Bary was well enough to talk, and he even joked with his wife, who was at his bedside.

An hour later, however, there was a sudden drop in blood pressure and his heart stopped beating. All attempts to revive him were ineffectual, and at six thirty Monday morning Gerald de Bary was pronounced dead.

The pathological examination which followed showed him to have been a man in good physical condition at the time of the bite with no abnormalities which might have contributed to, or hastened, his death. Under normal conditions, the puff adder is a comparatively sluggish snake, and it can only be assumed that the one that killed De Bary struck in what it considered to be self-defense when the zoo director accidentally thrust his arm into the cage.

One of the strangest poisonous snakes of Africa and Asia is the spitting cobra (*Naja nigricollis*). It grows to a length of approximately seven feet and resembles other cobras in all respects except in its manner of defense.

The spitting cobra can bite in the conventional manner

by sinking its fangs into the flesh of animals it wishes to kill. When defending itself it rears to an upright position and ejects a thin jet of venom from each of its two fangs. The poison may travel for a distance of six to twelve feet, and if the snake's aim is true the venom hits the man or beast in the eyes. The result is temporary or permanent blindness coupled with extreme pain. This act of spitting venom is also practiced by the South African ringhals (*Haemachates haemachatus*). In any of the spitting snakes, it is purely a defensive measure and is not employed when the snake is searching for food.

Since no snake is able to purse its lips, the term *spitting* is somewhat misleading if the conventional definition of the verb is considered. To accomplish its feat the spitting cobra draws its head back, opens its jaws to expose the fangs, and then contracts the temporal muscles over the paired poison glands. This is done with such suddenness and force that the venom is ejected in jets much like water is squirted from a water pistol.

Upon striking the eyes of a warm-blooded animal the venom is quickly absorbed by the superficial blood vessels and attacks the conjunctiva. Blindness and extreme pain are the immediate result, and if the victim is unable to wash the eyes quickly with water, the loss of sight may be permanent.

The cages of spitting cobras are generally easy to spot in the snake house of any zoo because the protective glass windows separating the snakes from the human spectators are frequently spattered with streams of venom.

The jungle and wilderness country of Central and South America is extensive, and these sections of the western hemisphere are populated with just as many types of dangerous snakes as Africa and Asia. However, reported death rates from snakebite in the New World are hardly a tenth of that in Africa and Asia. The reason for this disparity is due largely to the wide variation of population density in these two geographical regions. Another factor to be considered is that better records are kept in such countries as India than in the outlying districts of South America.

One of the most deadly of all snakes found in the western hemisphere is the South American rattler (*Crotalus terrificus terrificus*). While a true rattlesnake in every sense of the word, there is one important difference. Its venom is neurotoxic, in contrast to the hemotoxic venom of North American species. Because of this it is one of the snakes used in the preparation of the polyvalent snakebite serum.

The fer-de-lance (*Bothrops atrox*) is the most abundant poisonous snake in the New World. It ranges from central Mexico through Central America and as far south as northeastern Argentina and is also found on the island of Trinidad. The name fer-de-lance is from the Creole-French meaning *head of the lance,* referring of course to the shape of the snake's head. In Central America the natives call it Barba Amarilla, which means *yellow beard,* because of a yellow wash of color on the underside of the lower jaw and neck. These snakes grow to a length of eight feet and are frequently found in the dense growth of banana plantations. It is here that the greatest number of bites are recorded.

The bushmaster (*Lachesis mutus*) is the largest of the pit vipers, growing to a length of twelve feet or more. Natives of Central America call them La Cascabela Muda meaning *the silent rattler.* The name is appropriate since they resemble a rattlesnake without the string of rattles at the tip of the tail. But the absence of rattles does not prevent the bushmaster from making its presence known by sound. When aroused it will often begin to vibrate the tip of its tail, and if it happens to be in dry leaves the sound produced will resemble that of a true rattlesnake. Other snakes, like the copperhead of North America, will sometimes resort to this practice of imitation.

Along with its superior size, the bushmaster has another distinction in that it is the only egg-laying member of the family Crotalidae. Like the mambas of Africa it has gained a reputation of being a snake that will attack a human intruder. Once in the jungle country south of the Panama Canal I was absolutely convinced that the bushmaster must undoubtedly be the most aggressive snake on earth.

The day was overcast and it had just stopped raining. As I walked along a trail I saw something tumbling about on the ground in a small clearing. As I drew nearer I saw it was a small Capuchin monkey, and my first guess was that it had been injured by falling from the branch of a tall tree. Just as I was bending over the tiny body I caught sight of a large bushmaster gliding straight toward me. Startled, I brought up the single-shot .20-gauge shotgun I was carrying and took quick aim. The load of number-seven shot hit the snake, and while it convulsed in a tangle of twisting coils I fumbled another shell out of my coat pocket. When I was sure the snake was dead I again turned my attention to the monkey, which by this time was also dead.

Slowly the pieces of the puzzle began to fit together. My guess was that the bushmaster had struck the monkey some distance away and the little fellow had scampered into the clearing before the poison took full effect. The snake was probably coming to collect what it thought was rightfully its and may not even have seen me standing there. I still doubt, however, that it would have turned away unless I had been able to stop it with the gun.

Drop for drop the venom is not particularly virulent, but what it lacks in toxicity is more than made up for in quantity. The fangs are long, and large amounts of poison are injected in a single bite.

One friend of mine who had traveled extensively in Colombia and Venezuela told of visiting a tribe of natives who practiced a strange rite concerning the bushmaster, or *surucucu* as the snake is known in parts of South America. At certain times of the year the tribal witch doctors conducted a ritual during which members of the tribe were supposedly rendered immune to the bushmaster. My friend, who was present at one of these ceremonies, said that the natives to be immunized were forced to submit to a deep incision made on the top of the right thigh. Into this was rubbed a gooey concoction that resembled pancake batter. From that moment on the recipient of the treatment could walk freely through the jungles, and any bushmaster that happened to be nearby would beat a hasty retreat. As proof of the efficacy of the witch doctor's magic the men who had been treated were given a large bushmaster to handle. According to my friend, the snake made no attempt to bite, but only struggled to get away. I asked if possibly the snake had been defanged, such as some of those used by the Hopi Indians of Arizona in their annual Snake Dance or some of the cobras used by "snake charmers" in India. My friend said that he had suspected that such was the case until he had an opportunity later to examine the bushmaster and found it to be a perfectly healthy specimen.

From a common sense viewpoint, such pagan proceedings would be about as dependable as the wearing of an asafetida bag around the neck to ward off the agues. The natives of that tribe apparently had faith in it, however, and it serves to show to what extent some people will go where snakes are concerned.

Europe is almost entirely free of venomous snakes, or those that constitute a threat to human life. There are two, however, that do have poisonous fangs, and these are the lebetine viper (*Vipera lebetina*) and the long-nosed viper (*Vipera am-*

modytes). A bite from either of these snakes causes suffering, but fatalities are rare.

Ireland, of course, has no snakes and while most stalwart sons of the Emerald Isle give full credit to good Saint Patrick, the herpetologist sees it as a geographical condition. The few snakes that might occasionally find their way across the Irish Sea from England would not survive long enough in the inhospitable reptile climate to find mates and establish a colony.

There are other major islands of the world that are without snakes. Important among these are New Zealand, Bermuda, and all of islands of Hawaii. The latter has one exception, and that is a tiny blind snake (*Typhlops braminus*), which is believed to have been accidentally introduced from the Philippines some years ago in a shipment of potted plants.

It is quite understandable why islands such as Ireland and New Zealand, so far from any tropical land mass, are able to remain snakeless, but Hawaii is more of a puzzler. All conditions there are ideal for almost any snake to thrive, but they simply are not there and seemingly never have been.

It might be reasoned that the Hawaiian Islands are so far removed from any mainland that nothing could reach them by natural means. Things did reach them, however, and all came from foreign places: grass seeds, coconuts, insects, birds, and then came man with his animals and all kinds of potted plants. Since snakes can fast for such long periods it is a wonder that enough of the more important varieties have not stowed away in cargos such as hay and grain to become established. Even today with refrigerated ships snakes from Central America frequently find their way into the ports of New Orleans and New York tucked away in cargos of bananas. They even manage to survive chemically fumigated warehouses that are used to hasten the ripening of the fruit

and frequently slither out of a bunch of bananas to the con-
sternation of longshoremen and dealers.

Careful inspection of all incoming cargo is of fairly recent
design, and it is hard to see why man, with his slipshod
methods half a century ago, did not manage to bring all manner of dangerous and harmless snakes to the state of Hawaii.
One pregnant snake might produce fifty or more youngsters,
and these could form the beginning of a colony in a land
where the weather is always tropical and food is plentiful.
With any luck, however, the little blind snakes will be the
only serpentine travelers to homestead in America's fiftieth
state.

Another peculiar fact in the geographical distribution of
snakes is the absence of any poisonous species on the larger
islands of the Caribbean. Cuba, Hispaniola, Jamaica, and
many of the lesser islands have a normal snake fauna of
the harmless varieties, but no poisonous ones. Oddly enough,
there exists a distinct inconsistency in the distribution of
snakes in these islands, for the deadly fer-de-lance (*Bothrops
atrox*) and coral (*Micrurus corallinus*) are found in the
Windward Islands as well as in Trinidad. One might well
wonder why these species do not continue on through the
Leewards and then west throughout the larger islands. It
would seem that if these snakes could be transplanted from
one island to another in the Windwards, perhaps being borne
on logs and other floating debris, they could continue their
island-hopping all the way across the Caribbean.

Australia on the other side of the world is a continent generously endowed with both harmless and poisonous snakes.
The most dangerous of these are the taipan (*Oxyuranus
scutellatus*), death adder (*Acanthophis antarcticus*), and the
tiger snake (*Notechis scutatus*). The tiger, so named because
of its distinctive marking, is credited with having the most
potent venom of any land snake in the world.

4

SNAKE KILLERS

The snake clan has a host of enemies, and chief among these is man. Since the beginning of time he has made a practice of bashing the head of any snake that crosses his path, and as a rule he does so with little or no discrimination between dangerous and harmless varieties. But man is not alone in this. They are killed by certain animals, birds, and fish whenever the opportunity presents itself. Even snakes attack and destroy their own kind.

Most creatures kill snakes as a source of food. There are, however, exceptions and one of the most interesting of these is the whitetail or Virginia deer. This nimble-footed ruminant of eastern North America has no interest in eating snakes, yet, as man does, will occasionally kill a poisonous snake simply because the two happened upon the same place at the same time.

Naturalists who have found themselves in a favorable position to witness such a killing have described how the deer performs the feat. Upon sighting the snake the deer will prance toward it and then, bunching its four feet together, the deer bounces up and down as if it might be riding a pogo stick or bounding on a trampoline. As the deer dances, its sharp hooves chop the snake to pieces.

I have never actually seen this performance to an extent that I could swear to its validity, but if circumstantial evidence is to be considered then I would make a good witness. The incident I came *close* to observing occurred in northwest Florida. The time was midsummer and I was drifting in my bateau down a small stream that flowed into the Chipola River. The afternoon air was still, and long streamers of Spanish moss hung motionless from the limbs of twisted oaks and tall tupelos. I had been fishing for shellcracker and bream, and now with a well-filled stringer, I had laid my tackle aside and was simply drifting lazily along with the current observing the primeval swamp that seemed itself to be languishing in a siesta.

Now and then alligators and turtles would drop off logs and submerge in the coffee-colored stream, and an occasional water turkey would spread its wings and leave the snag on which it had been perched. Then, suddenly, the tranquility was broken by cracking and thumping sounds that came from behind a dense tangle of underbrush on the left bank of the stream.

Roused from my lethargy, I dug the paddle into the water and brought the boat to a standstill. The noise continued, but I could see nothing. Hoping to get a better view, I stood up, and as I did so I upset my tackle box, which was on the seat beside me. Just as it clattered to the bottom of the boat I caught a fleeting glimpse of a deer bounding away into the fastness of the swamp.

My curiosity whetted, I steered toward shore and grounded the boat on a narrow sandbar. Pushing my way through the bushes I broke into a small clearing. For a moment I stood still and looked about, and then my eyes caught sight of a slight movement near a small palmetto. Walking toward it,

I saw a rattlesnake—or rather, what was left of one. While the snake was still alive, its cut and mangled body made it obvious that it would not be for long. I picked up a stout stick and finished killing it. Excluding the damage I caused to the head of the four-foot diamondback, there were nineteen distinct wounds on its body, and the spine was broken in at least two places.

At first I did not associate the deer with the mangled snake, but while I stood there puzzled and wondering I noticed the hoof marks in the soft earth. From this point it was simple to reconstruct the episode as it probably took place. The deer was probably browsing along through the swamp, perhaps on the way to the stream for a drink. When it walked into the clearing the rattlesnake became alert and drew itself into a coil while its string of rattles began to buzz. Had it been another type of animal, such as a bear or a fox, the chances are good the warning would have been quickly heeded. Almost any animal will change course to avoid a poisonous snake. I once took a nasty spill when a horse I was riding went into a frenzy upon sighting a snake that suddenly glided out onto the path in front of us. The deer, however, probably sighted the rattler in the clearing and realized that here was a chance to make a kill. It was no doubt in the process of prancing on the snake when I betrayed my presence by upsetting my tackle box.

Just why the deer would elect itself as high executioner of snakes and just how often it does so is one of those questions that a naturalist can only ponder in the light of his observations. I doubt that a deer would attempt to kill a snake encountered in dense underbrush or any place where it would have the advantage of concealment.

Domestic cats will occasionally make a reputation for themselves as snake killers, and many times they do so with no intention of eating their prey. I had a beautiful female cat who spent most of her lifetime caring for her latest litter of kittens. When she was not busy with her nursing chores she was quite content to lounge about in the sunlit garden, sharing her domain with an assortment of birds, rabbits, and squirrels. Never in the many years this cat lived with me did I ever see her attempt to catch any of the birds or other creatures. Her one exception to her self-imposed ban on hunting was snakes, and I suspect this came about when she detected that I was more than a little impressed with her first kill.

The back lawn ended with a boxwood hedge that shut off nearly five acres of what had at one time been a plum orchard. Passage of time, change of ownership, and the resulting loss of interest in plums had allowed the stretch of land to revert to nature, providing a natural retreat for birds and all manner of small animal life, including a considerable number of snakes.

The first time I saw my cat catching a snake was one warm spring morning. She backed through the hedge with her tail held high, and she was moving almost as fast as I had ever seen her move in a forward direction. She was holding an eighteen-inch copperhead by the tip of its tail and dragging it into the middle of the lawn. When she let go, she began circling it, hissing with fury. Obviously angry and perhaps somewhat bewildered by the rough treatment it was receiving, the copperhead drew itself into a coil and prepared to make a last-ditch stand.

For a minute or two the cat continued to circle the snake, striking out now and then with a feinting paw until she found the opening she was seeking. In a blur of motion she pounced, her jaws closing on the snake's neck just behind the head. She chewed and growled until the writhing coils relaxed and then walked serenely away without so much as a backward glance. Since this was the first time I had seen

her catch a snake, I naturally showered her with praise and
attention. Perhaps in her feline reasoning she decided she
had struck a resonant cord and repeated the act many times
during her life.

The animal that enjoys the most celebrated reputation as
a killer of snakes is unquestionably the mongoose. Had it
not been for that great storyteller Rudyard Kipling the mongoose probably would have remained about as anonymous as
the numerous other weasel-like creatures to which it is related. But in his story *Rikki-Tikki-Tavi* Kipling brought the
mongoose to the attention of the world by portraying it as a
skilled and courageous killer of the deadly cobras of India.

Despite popular belief, snakes form only a small part of
the mongoose's diet. It feeds primarily on rodents and birds,
supplementing this bill of fare with an assortment of frogs,
lizards, insects, and other small creatures. Occasionally, but
only occasionally, it catches and eats a snake, which sometimes is a poisonous one such as a cobra.

When a fight does occur between a cobra and a mongoose
the little weasel-like animal is able to give a good account of
itself, relying on speed and an inherent knowledge of the
cobra's method of attack. It darts back and forth in front of
the snake, badgering it into striking time after time until it
becomes weary. The mongoose then rushes in and grabs it
just behind the head and breaks the neck with its powerful
jaws.

Because of its reputation the mongoose is often subjected
to staged fights with cobras, but these exhibitions frequently
end in a draw with both combatants becoming too exhausted
to continue. For people who derive some sort of thrill from
watching caged animals battle to the death they would find
far more fast action by pitting a mongoose with a large rat.
The rat is one of its chief items of diet, and the battle is sure
to be fast and furious with the rat invariably the loser.

The mongoose is a familiar animal in the state of Hawaii. It was introduced there shortly before the turn of the century by planters who were being plagued by vast numbers of rats that were destroying valuable crops. The decision to import the mongoose was based on similar successful experiments on Caribbean islands around 1870.

When the mongoose arrived in the Hawaiian Islands it found the climate to its liking and, with no enemies to bother it, multiplied and flourished. Within a few years the rat population had been sharply reduced, but there was one serious side effect which the sponsors of the mongoose had not counted upon. The islands have always been a natural sanctuary for bird life in superabundance, and when there was no longer a fat young rat just waiting to be caught, the mongoose was quite willing to satisfy its appetite with birds. As a consequence, the avian population of Hawaii began to suffer, and the once-welcome mongoose today constitutes a continuing threat to the birds.

During World War II in the Pacific a young army lieutenant had been placed in charge of a small garrison on one of the islands. He soon found that the major problem was not the Japanese soldiers who still remained hidden on the island. Instead, it was a vast horde of rats that were upsetting the morale of the men under his command. They invaded all of the dwellings and crawled into the soldiers' bedding. At mealtime men with clubs had to be stationed at the ends of the mess tables to ward off the voracious creatures.

Recalling the success on other islands, the young lieutenant decided to see if he could relieve the situation by starting a mongoose colony on his island. When he attempted to word his radio message to headquarters in Australia, however, he found himself in trouble. He looked at the message he had written which read: *Request I be sent several mongooses.* Then, debating the plural, he changed his message to read: *Request I be sent several mongeese.* When this too did not look right he quickly rose to the occasion and penciled a message which he handed to the radioman. On his third try the enterprising young officer had simply worded his appeal to read: *Request that I be sent a mongoose and, by the way, send me several more.*

Birds are often predators of snakes, but whether they kill and eat a snake depends to a large extent upon the size of each. Even robins will not hesitate to gobble a tiny worm snake as well as the newly hatched of other species. There are three birds, however, that are much like the mongoose when it comes to a reputation for being dauntless killers of snakes. These are the secretary bird of Africa, the roadrunner of the southwestern United States and Mexico, and the seriema of South America. A fourth and serious contender for the title is the common wild turkey of North America.

The secretary bird wears the undisputed crown among the avian snake killers. This storklike bird grows to a height of about four feet, and although it can fly, it spends most of its time walking sedately across regions of low vegetation on the African veld in search of food. As with the mongoose, its diet is by no means restricted to snakes. Lizards, frogs, rodents, bird eggs, and even small birds are eaten. When it does chance upon a snake, however, it is quite willing to add this to its menu, and its skill at killing the serpent provides an interesting show for anyone fortunate enough to witness the performance.

A harmless snake is simply pinned down with a taloned foot until the secretary bird can grab it by the head with its beak and swallow it with the same ease that other birds swallow worms. Should the snake be a cobra, mamba, or some other poisonous species, the tall bird exhibits a great deal of caution. It spreads its wings and prances toward the snake, lashing out with its long bony legs. Although the snake will strike time after time, the secretary bird as a rule is skilled enough to fend off the blows with its wings so that the fangs slash harmlessly into the feathers. With each strike of the snake, the bird delivers a downward, ostrichlike kick with its foot. When the snake is completely exhausted the secretary grabs it close to the head and shakes it to death.

In the desert southwest portion of the United States and down into Mexico there is a long-tailed bird about the size of a small domestic chicken that is known as the roadrunner or chaparral cock. It is closely related to the cuckoos, but unlike its arboreal-nesting relatives, the roadrunner spends most of its time on the ground. Folklore is filled with the exploits of this plucky little bird's relentless war on such dangerous snakes as the sidewinders and western diamond-backs.

It is no fable that the roadrunner accounts for a large number of poisonous snakes. It lives in a region where poisonous snakes are plentiful, and they form as much a part of its diet as do lizards and insects. Most of the snakes the road-runner catches are small, but many farmers on both sides of the border stoutly maintain that the little chaparral cock will unhesitatingly attack and slay even the largest rattler. More elaborate tales of this bird's derring-do have it taking up residence near farms and actually protecting its human friends from snakes by warding off lethal strikes, sometimes at the cost of its own life.

Even more fanciful is a persistent yarn obviously concocted by someone who knew little or nothing about birds or snakes. Supposedly when a roadrunner happens upon a sleeping rattler, the bird forthwith begins to act with great stealth and ingenuity in an effort to capture the snake. According to the story, the cock collects bits and pieces of cactus and other thorny plants and swiftly erects a wall around the victim. When the task is completed the bird retires to a shady spot to rest and wait. Eventually the snake awakens and prepares to go about its way only to discover that it is hemmed in on all sides by a thorny barricade. The hapless serpent searches in vain for an exit until it is exhausted and dies of starvation. At this point the roadrunner dismantles its trap and proceeds to devour the dead rattler.

This belief, of course, is pure fantasy and completely illogical. In the first place a snake simply does not sleep so soundly as to permit all of this activity to take place around it without awakening. Secondly, it is not in the least dismayed or restricted by thorns. Its horny plates and scales enable it to glide freely through the densest bramble without a scratch. Nevertheless, it makes a good story to tell while sitting around the campfire at night on the desert.

Regrettably, the roadrunner does not possess a clean slate with sportsmen, for while it kills snakes and lizards and devours countless insects, it is also not adverse to eating quail chicks. For this reason many sportsmen will not hesitate to shoot it in the misguided belief that they are striking a blow for better hunting by eliminating a predator. Overlooked is the fact that each snake the roadrunner eats in its lifetime is potentially a destroyer of game birds when it reaches a size that will permit it to swallow an egg or capture a member of a nesting covey.

The common domestic swine probably accounts for more snakes than any other animal. Pigs and hogs are forever hungry, and while vegetables form the bulk of their diet they are especially fond of meat. To a hog, a snake, whether it be a fat corn snake or a water moccasin, is just something else to eat.

I once saw an old sow eat a five-foot diamondback rattlesnake alive. The snake had been prowling about the barn no doubt in search of rats and had trapped itself by falling into an empty fifty-five gallon oil drum. A farmhand found it and slipped a noose over its head. Taking it outside he removed the noose and tossed the snake over into a pig pen so I could see what would happen.

It was the middle of the day and the summer sun was hot. The snake drew itself into a tight coil and set its string of rattles buzzing. Instantly an old sow that had been dozing in the shade of a chinaberry tree scrambled to her feet and trotted toward the snake, followed closely by two shoats. One of the shoats reached the snake at almost the same time as the sow, and as she turned to drive the smaller pig away the rattler lashed out and struck her on the side of the head. She winced, but a moment later she had the snake in her mouth and noisily devoured it while the two younger pigs attempted to bite off the portion that had not yet been swallowed.

Various studies have been made to determine why swine are immune to snake venom, and the generally accepted theory is that the layer of fat that encases a pig's body retards the absorption of the venom. This may be true, but it does not account for the fact that razorbacks and lean pine rooters of the southern states also feed on poisonous snakes without apparent injury or fear. It is a well known fact that many small islands offshore from such states as Georgia and Florida have been virtually stripped of snakes once a drove of pigs is released on them.

The little spotted skunk of the southern United States also seems to possess an unusually high resistance to snake venom. They will occasionally eat rattlers and other poisonous snakes and even do so after being bitten one or more times while killing the snake.

To a lesser degree, there are numerous other creatures which make a practice of killing and eating both dangerous and harmless snakes. These include hawks, eagles, otters, turtles, alligators, and even domestic chickens. For the most part, however, they catch snakes on a haphazard basis and are not generally recognized as true snake killers.

Many species of snakes are cannibalistic by nature, with big ones eating smaller ones of their own kind. Some mother snakes will even eat their own young should they happen to cross her path.

There are numerous snakes that have endeared themselves to humans because of their reputation for destroying the noxious members of their own kind. Chief among these are the king snakes, of which there are more than a dozen different types. Again, as with the mongoose, roadrunner, and the secretary bird, the king snake enjoys a favorable reputation that is only partly deserved. Nevertheless, he does feed on other snakes and occasionally swallows one of the poisonous varieties.

The kings are widely distributed from Canada to South America. They range in size from the diminutive scarlet king snake (*Lamporpeltis elapsoides*), which grows to a length of hardly more than fifteen inches, to others that measure over five feet.

The diet of king snakes consists of rodents, lizards, birds, eggs, and other snakes. Eggs are simply swallowed as they are found, but with living creatures the king kills in much the same manner as boas and pythons. Its first act is to grasp the victim with its jaws and quickly throw several coils around the body. Death is brought on by prolonged constriction. In the case of a lizard or a mouse this may take only a few minutes, but should the prey be a large snake, the two may remain locked in a death struggle for an hour or more.

The kings seem to suffer no ill effects from the venom of poisonous snakes. They have frequently been observed to be bitten repeatedly by rattlers and water moccasins and other poisonous varieties.

In one battle I witnessed between a captive rattlesnake

and a king of equal size, the freshly caught specimens, each measuring about two and a half feet in length, had been placed in a large wire-enclosed cage. The rattler immediately took up station in one corner where it drew itself into a defensive position, its vibrating tail filling the air with a metallic buzzing. The king snake ignored the rattler for nearly half an hour while it explored the cage before it decided to fight.

Without warning the king's head lashed out, and the rattler was caught near the middle of the body. At the same instant the rattler struck, its fangs puncturing the king near the tail. For the next few minutes there was a tumbling mass of coils, during which time the rattler struck again and again. Throughout the struggle his tail maintained a steady buzzing, and as the battle waxed the king began to vibrate his own tail as if in silent mockery.

After a series of quick bites the king's jaws finally closed on the rattler's neck just behind the head. Then one coil after another was slipped deftly around the rattler, drawing tighter and tighter until the two almost seemed to be braided into one. The action became very slow from that point on through the following hour, and finally the rattler's bottom jaw went slack, and the tongue slipped out of the sheath and lolled motionless.

Slowly the king snake began to release its coils, and as it relaxed it explored the rattler's head as if cautiously searching for any signs of life. Apparently assured that none existed, it slipped completely free and glided over to the opposite side of the cage where it rested for nearly twenty-four hours. It made no attempt to swallow the rattler, probably deciding that it would be too much of a meal.

In the week that followed the king snake was carefully observed and appeared to be in good health. However, it made no attempt to eat, although several mice and smaller snakes were introduced to the cage. On the eighth day, however, it captured and swallowed one of the mice and continued to feed regularly thereafter for the next six months that it was kept in captivity. During this time it became docile, submitting to handling without protest unless it was bothered just after eating.

It is doubtful that if in the wilds a king snake would deliberately attack a venomous snake, or a harmless one for that matter, larger than it could expect to swallow. But this observation is contested by sponsors of the king snake's popularity, with many testifying to having seen kings deliberately attack and kill snakes twice their size. It is likely that in the cage test the king felt the rattler was in some way responsible for its confinement and was simply taking revenge. The experiment did prove that by constriction a king can kill a snake of at least equal size, and it proved, too, that it suffers no ill effects from venom.

5

SEA SNAKES

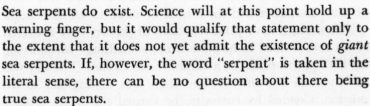

Sea serpents do exist. Science will at this point hold up a warning finger, but it would qualify that statement only to the extent that it does not yet admit the existence of *giant* sea serpents. If, however, the word "serpent" is taken in the literal sense, there can be no question about there being true sea serpents.

For some unexplicable reason there are no sea snakes in the Atlantic Ocean, but there are several dozen different species found in the Pacific and Indian Oceans, all belonging to the family Hydrophiidae. They range in length from two to twelve feet, and tests on laboratory animals have proved that some have venom fifty times more potent than that of the king cobra.

On the whole, all sea snakes look very much like their terrestrial relatives of the *Elapinae* group, which includes the cobras, kraits, and corals with their fixed fangs. They have scales and the familiar forked tongue, but there is one chief difference in their appearance: their tails are vertically compressed or paddlelike.

Sea snakes live chiefly in shallow bays and estuaries and

feed exclusively on fish. It therefore follows that they would possess a neurotoxic poison to attack the nerves and stun cold-blooded fish into submission far more quickly than if the venom were hemotoxic like that of the rattlesnake that feeds chiefly on warm-blooded creatures.

One exception to the true sea snake is a freshwater species, *Hydrophis semperi Garman.* This is found in Lake Taal on the island of Luzon in the Philippines. In a sense, it might be likened to the Lake Nicaragua shark, *Carcharhinus nicaraguensis,* which is the only true shark known to inhabit freshwater exclusively.

At certain times of the year sea snakes are to be found congregating on the surface of the ocean in astronomical numbers. A tramp steamer once passed through a vast shoal of them that stretched for a mile or more in all directions.

There was a navy pilot who told of passing over a stretch of sea that seemed to be alive with "something" while flying his PBY patrol plane on a mission near Ceylon. The day was calm and so was the sea, and there was no urgency to his mission. Goaded by curiosity, he turned the plane around and once again flew over the strange area. Even from an altitude of fifty feet and at a reduced speed of eighty knots he could still not tell what was causing the disturbance. Defying all rules prohibiting unnecessary landings at sea, he headed into the wind and landed on the surface right in the middle of the disturbed patch of ocean.

When the plane had come to a standstill, he and his fellow crew members went back to the blisters and looked into a boiling and twisting mass of snakes.

"There must have been millions of them," the pilot related. "Most were longer than my leg and as big around as my wrist. They were striped with black markings, and none seemed to be going anywhere in particular, just squirming around on the surface of the water."

One of the members of that patrol plane crew reached over the side and foolishly caught one of the snakes. Fortunately it made no effort to bite, but it did struggle to escape in much the same manner as any freshly caught reptile. Science knows relatively little of sea snakes and their habits. There are conflicting reports as to their willingness to bite. Oriental net fishermen frequently dredge them up in considerable numbers while fishing in shallow waters close to shore, and as a rule simply toss them back over the side with no more concern than a Grand Banks fisherman returning trash fish to the sea.

Again, skin divers and people wading along the shallow waters of the western Pacific shores have reported the sea snake to be as aggressive as a mamba or cobra. People who have been bitten by sea snakes have often died because the bite was not connected with the fatal illness that may take several hours to develop. For example, should one step on a snake while one is wading in shallow water in search of crabs or shellfish, there may be felt only a small stinging prick such as would be made by a sea urchin spine or sharp splinter of wood. Later, a feeling of intoxication may descend on the victim, and his speech may become slurred and a stiffness of muscles follows. Unless he suspects that he has been bitten by a poisonous snake the victim may believe that he is having a heart attack, as the breathing becomes more labored and the jaws refuse to operate. Eventually the predominant symptoms will be those of bulbar poliomyelitis and should be treated accordingly with the aid of a respirator.

No one on the Atlantic or Pacific side of the United States need have any fear of sea snakes except along the lower coast of California where one species of this snake is known to appear in spotted locations, ranging on down the coast of Mexico.

Because the moray eel is found on both sides of North

America this has fostered the idea that the sea is filled with dangerous serpents in both Atlantic and Pacific waters. But the truth is that neither is the moray a snake, nor is its bite venomous.

Skin divers and fishermen who have encountered the moray may be quick to take issue with this statement, but the facts are true. No eel, the moray included, possesses venomous fangs. This means in no way, however, to disregard the danger of a bite from a moray eel. These scaleless creatures grow to a length of ten feet or more and larger around than a man's thigh. Unless molested they seldom bite humans, but when they do their tooth-studded jaws can inflict serious injury. Perhaps because of their snakelike appearance and because of the severity of their bite they have long been considered to possess venomous fangs. But their teeth are no more dangerous than those of any other fish of equal size, and the moray does not possess venom glands. Certain ones of the more than twenty species of moray eels of the family Muraenidae are known to be poisonous if eaten, and this probably accounts for the wide belief that these eels are venomous.

In all of the western hemisphere there are but two poisonous lizards: the gila monster of the desert southwest section of the United States and the beaded lizard of Mexico and Central America. Both are thick-bodied creatures that grow to a length of almost two feet and, as the name implies, have scales that resemble beads.

Although gilas and beaded lizards are chunky and appear to be sluggish when undisturbed, they are capable of sudden and rapid movement. Instead of being in the upper jaw as with snakes, the fangs of these poisonous lizards are in the lower jaw. And unlike the hypodermic needles of the pit vipers, they are grooved and connected with venom glands. The jaws of both lizards are powerful, and the poison is

virulent enough to cause death to a human adult if injected
in sufficient quantity.

Gila monsters and beaded lizards feed on snake and bird
eggs, small rodents, and other lizards. In periods when food
is plentiful they store fat in their tails, which can grow nearly
half as large as the entire body. When food is withheld they
can subsist on this stored fat for nearly a year.

6

ROSS ALLEN

Here in the middle of the twentieth century there can be little doubt that the most colorful and widely known figure in the field of American herpetology is Ross Allen, of Silver Springs, Florida.

He has been on radio and television shows, featured in many movies, and he has written so many magazine articles and had so much written about him that his name has almost become synonymous with snakes. Most people who visit the Reptile Institute at Silver Springs or watch Ross Allen on television as he captures a large alligator or extracts the venom from a six-foot diamondback rattlesnake see the man only as a sort of P. T. Barnum of the herpetological world.

True, Ross Allen is a showman, and his profession has not only made him famous but also earned him a fortune. At the same time he is a scientist and a naturalist whose name will be listed with John James Audubon, Ernest Thompson Seton, Daniel Carter Beard, and other greats who have contributed so much to the general public's interest in wildlife and the outdoors.

When one watches the stocky and muscular director of the

Ross Allen Reptile Institute moving about the compound dressed in khaki pants, boots, and white shirt one is likely to get the impression that here is a backwoodsman, a typical Florida cracker, who just *happened* to find a good way to make a living by entertaining tourists. This was my impression when I first met him shortly after World War II. In the years that have passed, however, I have learned more and more about this amazing man and his success story.

Instead of being born of pioneer stock in a rustic log cabin in the piney woods of Florida and growing up in the wilds, Ross Allen was born on January 2, 1908, in the heart of Pittsburgh, Pennsylvania, the son of very normal and urban parents. His father, Charles Allen, was a newspaperman who planned for his son to follow in his footsteps. But in 1919 an attack of influenza and pneumonia almost cost Ross Allen his life, and the doctor suggested that he be withdrawn from school and encouraged to take long hikes to speed his recovery. This respite from the classroom gave him an opportunity to explore the woods and learn to love wildlife. He caught snakes and lizards and shot squirrels and crows, and as with many embryonic naturalists he decided to become a taxidermist.

In 1924 his journalist-father found work in Florida in the town of Winter Haven. The family moved south, and the then sixteen-year-old Ross Allen felt he was in a seventh heaven in this tropical setting with its dense forests and almost year-round summer.

In that year all of Florida was on the move. A group of real estate developers were busy pumping up a swamp to make a village called Miami, and thousands of people were coming south to enjoy a winter in the sun and drink orange juice from fruit plucked from nearby trees. Tourists, land developers, and vast amounts of money were pouring into the state, and it seemed that anyone with a willingness to do anything could earn a fortune. Highways and railroads were being built, and towns with paved streets were springing up in places where previously there had been only a log cabin or a turpentine still. People who owned land *as far as they could see* were being offered unbelievable prices for just a few acres.

During this period in Winter Haven, Ross Allen did three things. He attended school, taught people how to swim, and caught animals. If the Florida boom of the middle twenties had continued, he might have graduated from high school and gone on to college. But the period of fantastic land speculation came to an end, and the Allen family, with young Ross in tow, moved to Ohio. The Buckeye State, however, failed to hold the interest of the twenty-one-year-old naturalist, and ten days later he decided to return to his adopted state of Florida.

The year was 1929 and the United States was slipping into the great depression, certainly not an optimistic year for a young man with only the barest formal education and practically no money with which to venture into the field of business. With jobs at a premium, Ross Allen turned to the subject he knew best, taxidermy. He found that although part of the nation was standing in breadlines and men were willing to work from sunup to dark at hard manual labor for a single dollar, there were still a few people who had enough money to spend the winters in Florida. He found, too, that they were eager to buy things such as stuffed alligators, turtles, and small animals to take home as souvenirs. What was more important, he discovered that an increasing number of people who came to his establishment in Winter Haven to buy the stuffed creatures were even more interested in standing around observing the few living specimens which he kept in pens. As his menagerie grew he found these tourists willing to pay a fee to look at the collection of wildlife.

Before a year had passed, however, Ross Allen had to leave Winter Haven. He was never able to determine how it happened, but one night about twenty-eight of his alligators escaped and infiltrated the town. Most were small, measuring from two to four feet in length. Nevertheless, when some of the escapees found their way into stores and gardens, the people of Winter Haven demanded that Ross Allen either close his zoo or take his collection elsewhere.

He rounded up most of the escaped alligators and took them and his other wildlife to a friend in the country, who boarded them while Allen scouted the state for a place that would draw a goodly number of tourists and also be receptive to a zoological park.

He found Silver Springs was a natural gathering place for tourists journeying through the state. Here for a small fee they could step aboard a glass-bottomed boat and gaze down through crystal-clear water into a vast freshwater spring that flowed from great depths in the earth and daily poured over five million gallons of water into the Oklawaha River.

When Ross Allen opened his Reptile Garden here, a large percentage of the visitors paid an additional fee to walk about the jungle compound and look at pits and cages filled with alligators, snakes, and animals indigenous to Florida.

The reptilian jailbreak in Winter Haven was perhaps the best thing that ever happened to Ross Allen, for after the relocation to Silver Springs he became financially successful doing what he liked most—the catching and displaying of animals and reptiles for people who were interested in the subject.

When the clouds of World War II began to gather, the top brass of the military foresaw that servicemen were going to be exposed to snakebite and that the need for antivenin would be in far greater demand than it had ever been since its discovery. The United States entered the war in Decem-

ber of 1941, and Ross Allen wanted to volunteer for the
armed services, but the military medical staffs urged him to
remain at Silver Springs and continue to supervise the collection of venom so necessary for the production of the life-
saving antivenin that was becoming a standard part of
hospital supplies in far-flung battle theaters.

The tourist who watches a herpetologist "milking" a snake
is apt to be impressed with the amount of venom that appears to be extracted from a single specimen. Actually, the
venom of snake after snake is often injected into a single
glass container, and when several dozen have contributed
their share it can be deceiving to the uninitiated. The average adult snake such as a rattler yields only about half a
teaspoonful per milking.

Snake venom is pale orange in color and almost clear.
Soon after it has been extracted it must be put through a
high-speed centrifuge which separates bacteria and foreign
matter from it, and then it is lyophilized into a fine powder.
This dehydrated venom makes gold look as cheap as pig iron
by comparison, for today it sells at nearly $1,000 per ounce!
During the war years Ross Allen personally handled 73,960
poisonous snakes. While he did not receive $1,000 per ounce
then, he was paid a handsome price for the venom, and people were continuing to visit his Reptile Institute in growing
numbers. But just as a sailor on a landing barge at Nor-
mandy or a Marine hitting the beach at Iwo Jima, Ross
Allen risked his life, and he came perilously close to losing
it in the early days of 1944.

The incident occurred on February 26 of that year, while
he was on a snake-collecting trip near the west coast of Florida. Leaving the highway, he and two companions drove
about two miles back along a sand-rutted road that led to the
house of a man who supplemented his income by catching

snakes. The catcher had recently captured a five-foot diamondback rattlesnake and was holding it in a small box.

Before agreeing to buy the snake, Ross Allen wanted to
examine it, so he opened the box and dumped the snake out
on the ground. Deciding the reptile was in good condition
and worth the price the owner was asking, he placed his
snake hook on the reptile's head and leaned over to grasp
its neck in the same manner in which he had picked up thousands during his life. Just at the crucial moment, however,
his foot slipped and the hook slid backward freeing the
snake's neck. Instantly, it struck. This was not a typical
strike, but rather a sideward blow that sent both fangs into
the base of Allen's left thumb.

This was the fourth time he had been bitten since becoming interested in snakes. One bite had come from a water
moccasin and the other two had been from rattlers, but in
each case the amount of venom injected had been small and
the effects were not serious. This time, however, Allen knew
the bite was deep, and he felt from the beginning that it
might be serious. But he exhibited a calm approach to the
situation, continued his capture of the snake, and confined it
in a container. Only then did he apply a tourniquet and
lance his hand in three places.

While one of his companions drove the car, Allen, with
the assistance of the other, began to apply suction to the
wound. The three knew they were in a serious predicament.
Not only were they a considerable distance from medical
help, but on the way into the woods the car had become
bogged down in loose sand, and it had taken much shoveling
and pushing to get the wheels free. This same treacherous
stretch of sandy road still lay ahead of them. Should the car
bog down again the delay could well spell the end of Ross
Allen's life.

The driver made a wise choice as they approached the bad place in the road. Instead of trying to risk another bog-down, he steered off into the pines and literally made another road through the trees and dense underbrush.

Half an hour after being bitten, and despite the first aid treatment, Allen became paralyzed and was able only to talk. Upon reaching the hospital in Ocala he was immediately given 30 cc. of antivenin. During the first two days, attending physicians made nearly fifty incisions in an effort to draw off the venom, and plasma and whole blood transfusions were administered. At one point, about fifteen hours after being bitten, Allen had sunk so low as barely to be able to lift his eyelids. Morphine had to be administered from time to time to relieve pain. Severe swelling spread over most of his upper body, and he was unable to eat or drink for three days. At no time, however, did he lose consciousness. Thirst was his most serious complaint, but he reported that when he was given water it tasted very salty, much like sea water. Crushed ice placed in his mouth seemed to be the only way to alleviate the thirst satisfactorily.

On the fourth day it was noticed that gangrene had developed in the vicinity of the bite, and much of the decayed flesh of his thumb had to be cut away. Nervous tremors of his legs, abdomen, and face continued for nearly a week, and it was two months before he felt that he had successfully recovered from the effects of this rattlesnake bite.

In the next eight years Ross Allen's Reptile Institute at Silver Springs flourished, and his fame continued to spread. During this time he received five more snakebites, but none of them approached the seriousness of the one in 1944. None, that is, until 1952 when another rattlesnake singled him out for a target. How the accident occurred and the treatment administered were published in an article in the *Journal of* *the Florida Medical Association,** and most of that article, beginning with Allen's personal report follows:

"This was my worst snake bite. I was tired when it happened—too tired after a long hard summer season. There were more snakes to be milked, but I decided to take a little nap in the laboratory. Instead of sleeping, however, I got an idea about a new way to milk cobras; so thus inspired, I put on my snake-proof boots and went into the milking pen. I milked two or three cobras as an experiment, found that the new method worked and then proceeded to put all the cobras —60 of them—in the pen where I could reach them for individual milking. While moving around in the back part of the milking pen, I noticed an eastern diamondback rattlesnake that was badly frightened and belligerent. I therefore pushed him into the corner with my snake hook.

"A minute later I was having trouble getting a cobra off the snake hook and did not see this pugnacious 6 foot rattlesnake sneaking up on me. The first thing I knew, I heard and felt the snake's fang in my leg above the boot. Momentarily he was stuck there, and I knocked him free with the snake hook. It was hard to believe the snake had come from a distance of 7 feet to attack me and had struck more than half his length at a 45 degree angle to a height of 22 inches. I pushed the rattlesnake clear across the pen and opened the door to the laboratory. I had trouble closing the door because a cobra got in the way; so I had to lift him up with a snake hook and put him back through the door before closing it. I examined the bite. I found one deep fang puncture, but there was no pain or other symptoms at this 30 second period. Nevertheless, I made a deep cut with my lance and started suction with the vacuum kit.

"This was my tenth snake bite. Some bites had been mild, and three serious. From these experiences I had believed that

* Watt and Pollard, "Case of Serious Florida Diamondback Rattlesnake (*Crotalus adamanteus*) Bite," *The Journal of the Florida Medical Association,* 41:367–370 (Nov.), 1954.

the seriousness of a snake bite could be determined by sudden pain and the amount of swelling. But this time I was to learn differently. After two minutes had elapsed and there was no pain, only a slight numb feeling, I began to think that I had escaped with another mild bite, but at the end of approximately five minutes my facial muscles began to twitch. So I phoned my wife to come and take me to the hospital. I called my associates to help apply more suction, tie a tourniquet and made additional cuts. Approximately four minutes later it was difficult to talk plainly, and it was hard to walk to the car just outside the laboratory building. Other muscles were beginning to twitch rapidly. Still there was no pain.

"By the time I had reached the hospital I was so paralyzed that I could not walk at all, or even move my feet. It was apparent to me now that I had received so much venom that it had numbed the nerves, therefore, the lack of pain. The neurotoxic factor in the diamondback rattlesnake venom was causing my flesh to jump and twitch with the same feeling as of electricity charging through. The muscle twitching became steadily worse, and it was the most uncomfortable experience I have ever had with snake bite, but was compensated by the lack of pain. I was worked on for over an hour in the emergency room before being transferred to a room. I can recall only vaguely what happened the next six days; however, I do recall that at various times everything appeared to be yellow. When my mind became clear, I complained about the ice packs. The packs were removed. The pain soon became intense, and I requested replacement of the ice packs on my leg. The muscle twitching continued for several days, and I remember thinking when it finally stopped that I was just as tired as if I had run a hundred miles. What went on and was done for my physical condition is a matter of hospital record. I certainly cannot remember it accurately. I know that when I could finally raise my head and look at my leg, it was swollen and black, and I could not move it. When recovery warranted attempting to move the leg, extending it downward while trying to stand was so painful that I could not stand the pain over half a minute.

"After 22 days in the hospital and 102 more days of gradual recovery at home, a total of 4 months, I was able to go back to the Reptile Institute for a partial day's work.

"In this case I learned that immediate pain does not always result from the bite of a Florida diamondback rattler. This case also illustrates the value of research. Undoubtedly I survived only because I had available the best of modern scientific treatment. I cannot help feeling a great deal of satisfaction at having survived a most serious, often fatal type of snake bite; but brother, I don't want any more!"

Hospital Record of Case

This 43 year old white man was admitted to the hospital about 35 minutes after the snake bite. He was unable to walk and complained of tingling of the hands and face, particularly around the lips. His speech was affected; he was weak and nervous. Physical examination showed the heart to be normal in position and size with no murmurs; the lungs were clear; the liver and spleen were not palpable. The blood pressure was 100 systolic and 70 diastolic. The inner surface of the right leg at the knee showed a dark area about 1 inch in diameter. This immediate area around the fang puncture was excised, and the patient was given five ampules of Antivenin. He was then given a transfusion of 500 cc. of whole blood. Suction cups were used intermittently for about 10 hours on small incisions surrounding the fang puncture. Three hours after the accident the patient was complaining of intense pain in the right leg and chest.

In accordance with the recommendation of Andrews and Pollard,* the right leg, ankle to groin, was kept in ice packs for eight days.

* Andrews, E. H., and Pollard, C. B., "Report of Snake Bites in Florida and Treatment: Venoms and Antivenoms," *J. Florida M. A.*, 40:388–397 (Dec.), 1953.

Twenty hours after the victim was struck by the snake his right leg, calf to groin, was badly swollen and almost completely black. The swelling started to decrease on the fifth day. By the eleventh day swelling and cyanosis were only slight.

During the period from the second day to the sixth day in the hospital the icterus index fluctuated between 6.8 and 11.2. The highest value was shown on the third day.

On the second day the patient complained of an intense itching of the back and arms. This condition was completely relieved and controlled by 25 mg. of Benadryl three times a day.

Penicillin, 400,000 units, and combined tetanus–gas gangrene antitoxin, 3,000 units, were administered the first day. The penicillin dose was repeated the second day. Infusions of 1,000 cc. of 5 per cent glucose were given on the first and second days. Whole blood transfusions, 500 cc. each, were given on the first, second, fourth and sixth days. One vial of Combiotic was given on each of the fifth, sixth, seventh and eighth days. Frequent doses of Demerol were required for pain. The position of the patient was changed every few hours.

The daily temperature ranged from 97 to 103 F. during the 22 days of hospitalization. The lowest temperature was on the third day, while the highest range occurred from the fifth day through the eighth day. During the last four days in the hospital the temperature was normal. The pulse rate varied from 72 to 115. Except for high albumin, urine specimens were practically normal.

Particularly noteworthy in this case is the absence of tissue necrosis at the site of the bite.

When the patient was discharged from the hospital on the twenty-second day, a slight edema of the right ankle and pain in the calf of the leg persisted. He was able to walk a few steps, with difficulty. Numbness and tingling of the upper lip, which developed in a few minutes after the snake bite, were still sensed by the patient when discharged. He was confined to his home for a period of 102 days before he was able to return to work for part time duty.

7

PROTECTION

Whenever a case of poisonous snakebite is reported by newspapers in any given community there is sure to be a sort of shock wave that follows the accident. Always a certain group of people will suddenly become *snake conscious* and try to find ways and means to protect themselves and their loved ones from a similar accident. Letters and phone calls go to newspapers, nearby zoos, and such public protective agencies as the police, fire, and health departments. The queries generally fall into two main categories. One group asks for the best ways to avoid being bitten by a snake, and the other wants to know what is being done to protect the community from such hazards. There is also a smaller and perhaps somewhat more pessimistic group that assumes the worst is inevitable and wants to know what should be done once the snake has struck.

It seems to be something of a commentary on human nature when one considers that in today's world, which is steadily becoming more and more mechanical, people have learned to accept and almost ignore highway slaughter day after day, but they are spurred to serious attention when once in a very great while someone is bitten by a snake. The man who occasionally leaves a party with one or more too many highballs and tries to see how fast he can drive home is likely to take elaborate precautions against snakebite the next time he takes his family on a woodland outing.

Nevertheless, human nature being as it is, man has an instinctive fear of injury or destruction from some of nature's more natural forces, such as an attack by wild beasts, a strike of lightning, or a bite of a snake. He will often go to great labor and spend large amounts of money to protect himself from such hazards.

I remember that once when I was in the forestry service a twelve-year-old boy was fatally bitten by a water moccasin while catching tadpoles in a pond near a small town. A week later at the city commission meeting a group of excited citizens appeared with a plan to rid the township and its environs of the *deadly menace* of poisonous snakes. The petitioners demanded that all vacant lots, woodland areas, and grassy fields surrounding the city be put to the torch.

In that tempestuous meeting the voices of well-meaning but ill-advised citizens were more powerful than the words of experts, and in the harrowing week that followed, the scorched-earth plan was put into effect. Acre upon acre of meadow and woodland was systematically burned. When the atrocity was completed, the town was ringed with an ashen girdle of ugly black land. Gone were most of the birds, rabbits, chipmunks, and other creatures that had always been part of the local scene. For days the wind wafted ashes and smoke across the town and soiled washed clothes that had been hung out to dry. Nearly a week later an all-night rain extinguished the final embers, and the following morning a rattlesnake struck a pedigreed cocker spaniel squarely in the middle of the town's best residential district. The snake had taken shelter beside a barbecue pit. It struck the dog on the muzzle, and the cocker was dead within an hour.

When the burning was done, the town fathers took a look at the destruction and wondered if they had acted wisely. The pond where the water moccasin tragedy had taken place was still there and so were its inhabitants: the turtles, frogs —and snakes!

The average forest fire seldom kills many snakes. This is true because the snake knows it cannot race away swiftly like the deer or take wing like a bird. As a result, instinct has taught it to seek shelter whenever its sensitive olfactory system catches the first faint whisp of smoke drifting through the woods. All about its range, whether it be the flat piney woodlands of Florida or the brambled and rock-strewn hillside of New Jersey, every snake has its own list of secret shelters. It may be a tunnel dug by a gopher turtle or a fissure in a rocky ledge where it might have passed the previous winter's period of hibernation. Only on rare occasions when fire threatens will a snake be caught too far off base to reach one of these hideouts. Because it can go for long periods of time without food or water, it is content to remain safely snuggled away until the ashes have cooled. Only then will it emerge to seek a new range.

There seems to be no end to the attempts some people will make to protect themselves from the fancied menace of snakes. Not far from where I live there is a beautiful secluded lake surrounded by cypress trees, live-oak hammocks, and pine forest. Half a dozen families from nearby cities have bought large sections of property fronting the lake and built deluxe cottages that afford a solitary retreat from the workaday world. On one of the lakefront lots there stands today a monument to one man's stupidity.

The man was invited to spend a weekend at the lake with one of his business associates. He fell in love with the tran-

The anaconda is the world's largest snake and the longest land animal alive today. Reliable reports put its length at greater than forty feet. It is found in and around streams and lakes in tropical America.

Author photographing five-foot diamondback rattlesnake, in shadow of palmetto fronds, at left of picture. This was taken moments before the picture of the strike.

Photo by Helm

Diamondback rattler strikes at author's foot (lower right corner) missing its target by scant inches.

Photo by Helm

Eastern diamondback rattlesnake (*Crotalus adamanteus*) coiled and ready to strike. String of rattles can be seen buzzing at right of head.

Photo by Helm

Author, who was bitten by a timber rattlesnake while on a photographing expedition in Georgia, receives first aid treatment administered by his wife.

Photo by Helm

Author holding boa constrictor which moments later maneuvered its coils around his body necessitating forceful removal by author's wife.

Photo by Helm

Copperhead moccasin *(Agkistrodon contortrix)* becomes alert at the approach of a human. This pit viper will strike readily, but his venom seldom causes death to humans.

The Russell's viper *(Vipera russellii)* is the most dangerous viper in southeastern Asia. This species causes the second largest number of snake bites in Asia. The venom has been used for many years in medicine as a blood coagulant.

Photo by Thornton, Courtesy Miami Serpentarium

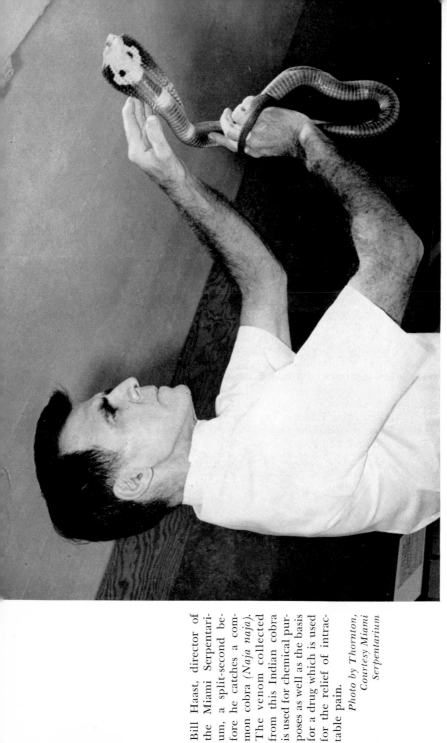

Bill Haast, director of the Miami Serpentarium, a split-second before he catches a common cobra (*Naja naja*). The venom collected from this Indian cobra is used for chemical purposes as well as the basis for a drug which is used for the relief of intractable pain.

Photo by Thornton,
Courtesy Miami
Serpentarium

Puff adder (*Bitis arietans*) is one of Africa's most dangerous snakes. This is the type snake that caused the death of Gerald de Bary, director of the Hogle Zoological Gardens, Salt Lake City, Utah, in 1964.

Photo by Thornton,
Courtesy Miami
Serpentarium

Photo by Helm

Water moccasin *(Agkistrodon piscivorus)* resting on mud bank of southern stream. When excited this snake often opens mouth wide, exposing white interior, which is why it is also known as the cottonmouth.

Cottonmouth moccasin in the process of swallowing a smaller snake. Tail of victim can be seen protruding from moccasin's mouth.

Courtesy Ross Allen's Reptile Institute

Photo by Helm

Three foot water snake resting on a log after shedding its old skin. Sometimes snakes are able to shed their skins as easily as a glove being stripped from a hand. Again, the process may require several days.

Eastern Coral snake *(Micrurus fulvius fulvius).*

Courtesy Ross Allen's Reptile Institute

Ross Allen holding eastern diamondback rattlesnake while lecturing at U. S. Naval Air Base at Jacksonville, Florida.

Small kit for use in first aid treatment of snake bite. When closed, entire kit is not much larger than a 12-gauge shotgun shell. Cups are made of rubber and used to draw out venom.

Courtesy Cutter Laboratories

Photo by Thornton, Courtesy Miami Serpentarium

Bill Haast and his wife, Clarita, force feeding a 12-foot king cobra *(Ophiophagus hannah)* at the Miami Serpentarium.

*Photo by **Helm***

Bill Piper, owner of the Everglades Wonder Gardens at Bonito Springs, Florida, pauses beside truck with a bag of recently captured snakes. Photo was made on expedition into Big Cypress Swamps.

*Photo by **Helm***

Dan Landt demonstrates use of snake hook in capturing a large diamondback rattler. Such hooks are employed to avoid injuring valuable specimens.

Opposite at top: Pocket size kit for use in first aid treatment of snake bite.

Opposite at bottom: Rattlesnake mouth opened wide to expose fangs.

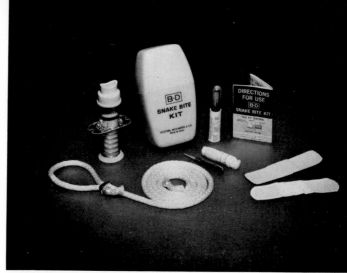

Courtesy Becton, Dickinson & Co.

Photo by Helm

Author's wife reluctantly submits to being photographed on her first try at holding an indigo snake. These snakes grow to a length in excess of eight feet and are favorites of collectors because they thrive in captivity.

Photo by Helm

Author, wearing snake-bite-proof boots, places foot on back of four-foot water moccasin to demonstrate inability of fangs to penetrate specially treated leather. Snake's venom can be seen streaming down side of boot just above the shank.

Photo by Helm

quillity, and early the following week he bought a large lot. In due course he had trucks bring in countless tons of concrete blocks and unload them on his newly acquired property. Next followed a crew of bricklayers who were instructed to build a nine-foot wall of blocks.

Neighbors watched with growing curiosity as the walls grew, and when they were nearly complete a massive wrought-iron gate was hung at the rear. At this point someone decided to ask the newcomer the reason for the construction. The answer was to prevent snakes from entering the yard.

When it was pointed out that any snake, from the slim garters to chunky water moccasins, could enter the property from either the wide grill of the rear gate or the completely open waterfront, the newcomer admitted that he had not taken that into consideration. He paid off the laborers and left; more, I suspect, from embarrassment than failure. Today the block walls still stand green with moss, and the iron gate is red with rust.

It is, of course, possible to construct a fence or wall that would be nearly snakeproof, but if a large area is to be enclosed the project will be costly. Gates would have to be positioned with almost the precision of weather stripping. Even then, frequent inspections would be necessary to be sure that the warping of wood or cracking of cement had not left small openings. Snakes, both large and small, are frequently able to escape captivity by slipping through almost unbelievably small spaces.

An example of this Houdini-like ability to escape from seemingly escapeproof prisons was demonstrated to me one morning while bass fishing along a North Carolina stream. While walking along the bank I happened upon a small snake about fifteen inches in length. Its body was dull yellow in color and marked with numerous reddish brown bands.

I knew it was some type of harmless water snake, but since I was not sure exactly what kind, I propped my rod and reel against a tree and caught it. I wanted to take it home for further study, but I was faced with the problem of how to keep it until I was ready to leave. It was then that I remembered an empty quart milk bottle I had in the car. The bottle had a waxed cardboard stopper. In the center of the bottle top was one of those little punch-out sections that, when removed, left an opening just large enough to admit two soda straws. I removed this for ventilation and then threaded the snake down into the bottle. When it had settled down I replaced the stopper and secured it around the edge with a strip of adhesive tape. The snake was about as big around as my index finger, and the hole in the bottle top was hardly a third the snake's size in diameter.

Placing the bottle on the shady side of a tree I returned to the stream and continued fishing. On my way back to the car I stopped to pick up my snake, and to my surprise I found the bottle was empty. Examining the top I saw that the tape seal had not been broken, nor had the hole been enlarged. The bottle was exactly as I had left it except that my snake was gone. Puzzled, I tried unsuccessfully to force my finger through the hole. Just as I was about to continue on to the car I chanced to spot my little escaped prisoner. It was tucked tightly beside a rotten log. Still curious about its identity and also how he had managed his escape, I caught it a second time and returned it to the bottle.

When I reached home I placed the bottle on a table in my workshop, and after consulting a few keys I was able to determine that the snake was a particularly colorful specimen of the southern banded water snake (*Natrix sipedon fasciata*). For the next two hours I kept the bottled snake under more or less constant observation. At about four o'clock in the afternoon it again became bored with its glass prison and commenced to repeat its performance.

First it lifted its body until its nose was pressed against the tiny opening in the bottle top. Then the head seemed to compress and elongate itself, and after a few minutes of shoving and twisting it came through the opening. The rest of the body began to pour slowly through the hole. Once the head was free there seemed to be no struggle, but the part that was passing through the opening was tightly compressed, as if a string had been tied around a toy balloon. When it was free it glided across the table, and just as it was about to drop to the floor I caught it again. This time I took it out to the woods behind the house and let it go. I had seen the camel pass through the eye of a needle.

The property owner determined to keep snakes out of his garden would not only be forced to cope with serpents like my milk bottle prisoner, but most snakes can climb. Some of them can scale vertical walls providing there is enough vine and moss growth to form almost imperceptible protrusions to which its scales can cling. There are other ways, too, that a snake might enter. It might, for instance, ride in on a car.

A man I knew was once traveling in California, and one afternoon he was driving along a road that skirted a section of desert country. He stopped frequently to take photographs of the scenery, and every time he stopped and got out of the car he heard a peculiar buzzing sound. The man checked every part of his car that he thought might be causing the noise. It was not air from one of the tires or steam from the radiator, and the electrical system seemed to be in good working order. At least there were no warning lights on the dashboard glowing red. Thoroughly perplexed, the man drove into a service station and put his car on the grease rack. As the hydraulic lift was going up a large diamondback rattler dropped to the floor. How, when, or why the snake had lodged itself in the under part of the car is unknown, but when the deadly hitchhiker hit the floor and drew itself into a coil, the attendant smashed its head with a well-aimed jack handle.

Snakes will occasionally invade human domiciles by the most unexpected routes. One nocturnal fisherman angling on an Alabama lake kept his catch of crappies and bluegills in a burlap bag tied to the stern of his skiff. When he returned home in the small hours of the morning and emptied his catch in the kitchen sink he nearly fainted at the sight of a three-foot water moccasin that had somehow worked its way into the bag. In the few minutes of furious activity that followed he managed to kill the snake with the handle of a broom, but in doing so he succeeded in knocking out the kitchen window, breaking an electric mixer on the drain-board and rousing the whole household with the clatter of his struggle.

The newcomer to outdoor life, such as the camper who buys a tent, gas lantern, and other equipment, is often heard to ask the best way to avoid being bitten by a snake during his woodland junket. He might just as well ask how he can keep from cutting his finger with his pocketknife or burning himself with hot grease while frying fish over the coals of a campfire. The only logical answer is simply to *be careful!*

The boob who goes stumbling through the woods with no thought of anything but getting from one place to another may pass close to a number of snakes and some of them may be dangerous. Ninety-nine per cent of the time the snakes will sense his approach and glide away to safety. Occasionally, however, a snake will see no ready route of escape and elect to stand its ground. If the snake happens to be of a venomous variety and the boob passes too closely, the snake is quite likely going to strike.

In general, the outdoorsman in the United States has little to fear from snakes. The reason is that most of the dangerous varieties will follow one of two courses. They will first try to slip away to avoid detection. If surprised before they can escape they will make a stand and try to frighten the invader by vibrating the tail, hissing, and assuming menacing poses. Keeping the eyes open and the ears tuned to any unusual sound, then, are man's two most valuable means of protection from snakebite.

Most snakebites occur on the hands and feet, and the vast majority of the former could be prevented if a reasonable amount of caution were used. Each year many people are bitten while reaching into holes such as animal burrows, hollow spaces beneath the roots of trees, and among rocks.

Carelessly stepping over a log lying across the trail is a surefire way to invite a bite on the ankle if a poisonous snake is resting on the other side. Early settlers and those who explored the wilderness country learned much of their woodland skill from the Indian, and they were quick to adopt the red man's way of crossing a log. He first stepped on top of it, thus giving himself a chance to scan the ground on the other side before continuing.

People are bitten frequently because of the careless handling of snakes. Sometimes this is a case of ignorance, particularly with children. They see a snake moving along the ground, and if they have not been taught better, they think it would make a nice thing to play with. Again, a show of bravado on the part of someone who wants to impress his companions can lead to trouble. I once knew a man who had gained quite a reputation as an outdoorsman, and when off on a picnic or other outing he never missed a chance to demonstrate his knowledge of nature. He was forever picking up odd-looking insects, plucking lizards from fence rails, and, of course, capturing any snake he happened to see. An office picnic one summer afternoon almost proved to be his undoing.

The self-styled David Crockett was helping the other men unload baskets of food and tubs of ice from the automobiles. At the same time the ladies were setting a long table that had been placed by a brook that wound through the park. Suddenly there arose a clamor of squeals and shrieks from the distaff force, and the predominant word was *snake!*

The outdoorsman set aside his chore of the moment and strode rapidly to the rescue. The object of the excitement was a dark brown snake about two feet long that was resting in the shallow water of the stream. A couple of the men picked up sticks and were bent on killing it, but the intrepid nimrod waved them aside and announced that he would catch "the harmless water snake."

It was a water moccasin and it bit the man on his hand. That wound up the picnic and the outdoorsman spent the next ten days in the hospital.

There are times when a person is forced to walk through or work in dense underbrush, and such conditions warrant protection for the feet and legs. The best is a pair of stout boots that come almost to the knees. Any boot, rubber or leather, is good, but for the extra cautious there are at least two brands of snakeproof boots offered for sale in the United States. The leather is specially tanned so that it will repel the fangs of the largest rattler. Such boots are expensive, but well worth the money when the danger of snakes is acute.

Less expensive, lighter, and far cooler are simple canvas leggings. For greatest protection they should not be washed, since hot water and soap tend to soften the canvas.

One company even produces snakeproof pants which have a liner of mesh wire. Such a garb might be useful under certain conditions, but the best safety measure is still simply to keep a sharp lookout on the ground ahead.

8

WILLIAM HAAST

To be bitten by a poisonous snake even once in a lifetime is an experience never to be forgotten. To survive the bites of no less than eighty-four poisonous snakes, including the king cobra, the rattler, the cottonmouth moccasin, and the blue krait, puts a man in a highly unusual category. But such a man is William Edward Haast, director of the Miami Serpentarium.

In the past twenty years Haast has been struck by more poisonous snakes than any man alive, averaging over four bites per year. Could all of the venom that has been pumped into his body be collected and equally distributed it would be enough to kill several thousand adult humans. This fact has caused a lot of head scratching and tongue clucking from the medical world.

In most respects, Haast is a very normal hardworking and prosperous businessman in his midfifties who devotes most of his waking hours to work and study. He operates a thriving tourist attraction that annually draws large crowds of sight-seers and tourists who stare with a sort of morbid fascination as king cobras and other deadly snakes from the far corners of the world have their venom extracted as casually as cows being milked at a dairy.

What makes Bill Haast different is that a number of years ago he conceived the idea of turning his body into a human laboratory to prove a theory. It was his belief that the human body could be made immune to the bite of venomous snakes if controlled doses of that venom were injected at regular intervals. Early experimenters in France a century ago had the same theory, but their experiments with animals had always ended in failure. When men of science learned that here in the middle of the twentieth century a man was using his own body as a guinea pig they issued dire warnings and even pondered how they could invoke legal measures to prevent him from committing public suicide.

Haast listened to their warnings, evaluated their wisdom, and then continued injecting snake venom into his veins. Several years later he had knocked some well-founded medical dogmas into a cocked hat and in addition, by donating blood from his own immunized body, saved the life of person after person who had been bitten by poisonous snakes.

Haast was born in Paterson, New Jersey, on December 30, 1910. When he was eleven years old he acquired his first pet, a small and harmless garter snake. A year later, when he reached the age of twelve, he joined the Boy Scouts and while still a tenderfoot went on a jamboree with his troop. The more serious aspects of scouting appealed to young Haast, and while the others were enjoying the usual sports of camp life, he decided to make a try for a merit badge by living off the land on a survival hike which he planned to extend for several days.

His trip went well for the first two days. He filled his canteen from springs, slept on beds of pine boughs, and satisfied his appetite with meager rations from his packsack. Near midmorning on a Sunday, he wandered onto a hillside covered with huckleberry bushes. The bountiful crop of dark blue berries was enticing to the hungry young explorer. While he was picking them from the low bushes there was a sudden blur of movement, and then he felt a sting of pain just below his left elbow. Jumping back, Haast looked at the fang marks on his forearm, and then he saw the snake. He had read enough books and seen enough snakes to know that it was a timber rattler.

"Looking at the snake and the wound on my arm," said Haast, "I recall that I was surprised, but not angry."

His Scout first aid training had outlined the treatment for snakebite as prescribed by doctors in 1922. His first act was to apply a tourniquet, and then using a razor blade from his first aid kit he lanced the wound. Strictly adhering to the medical dictates of the time, he then plastered the incisions with potassium permanganate. In fact, he did just about everything that modern medicine now advises is harmful, including a long hike back to camp. When he arrived near noon he saw that the troop had just been seated for lunch, and not wishing to interrupt the meal, he made his way to the hospital tent, where he waited until someone happened to wander in. When it was learned that the young Scout had been bitten by a rattlesnake the word spread rapidly, and a few minutes later the officials had Haast on his way to a doctor in Paterson.

He recovered quickly with no serious aftereffects and became absorbed with an interest in snakes. Most of his spare time during the warm months was spent roaming the countryside around Paterson in search of specimens that he could capture and bring home for study.

In the years that followed, Haast tried his hand at a number of jobs, and during World War II he became a flight engineer with Pan American World Airways, serving in the Air Transport Command. It was a job that he found much to

his liking for several reasons. Not only did it pay good money
but it gave him a chance to travel extensively in Africa and
the Orient. Most important were the stopovers in out-of-the-
way places, the small airports of Africa and India, that provided him with the opportunity of wandering through
strange jungles and forests. He was soon bargaining with
local snake catchers, and time after time Flight Engineer
Haast landed at his home base in Miami with his luggage
well packed with an assortment of cobras, mambas, and
kraits.

In 1947 Haast reached a turning point in his life. Three
nearly omnipotent factors were guiding his destiny. He had
managed to accumulate a comfortable bank account for a
single man, and he had what was perhaps one of the largest
private collection of snakes in the United States. Finally, he
could no longer resist the urge to devote his entire time to
the study of snakes, and also he felt he could make a good
living by supplying the medical world in the United States
with cobra venom. At the time it was in short supply, and
the going price of the imported product was $1,500 per
ounce. With careful handling, he reasoned, he could beat the
foreign market and produce a better quality venom at a
lower price.

Resigning from his job with Pan American Airways, Haast
began construction of a laboratory just outside the city of
Miami on U. S. Highway 1. At this time in his life he made
two other important decisions. First, he married Clarita Mat-
thews, and then shortly thereafter decided that if he was going to make his living by extracting venom from cobras and
other deadly snakes he might do well to take some protective
measures from the bites he was confident would be an occu-
pational hazard to face as long as he stayed in business.

Medical science had long ago proved that snake venom injected into the human body via the fangs of a snake could be

counteracted by the injection of antivenin or serum, but no reliable proof had ever been established that the human body could be rendered immune. It was Haast's theory, however, that immunity was possible, and he set out to prove it.

His initial experiment was to dilute one drop of cobra venom with many times its volume in a saline solution and inject it into one of his veins. Minutes later he noticed a soreness in his throat, his eyelids became heavy, and his entire body felt weary. Soon, however, the discomfort was gone, and a short while later he was back to normal. As the year wore on he repeated the experiment, increasing the amount of venom with each subsequent injection.

Gradually word leaked out that Haast was experimenting with a program of self-immunization. When the curator of a large zoo heard of the experiment he urged Haast to give up the attempt immediately, explaining that horses injected in a similar manner for the manufacture of antivenin seldom live for more than two years once the injections are begun. Haast acknowledged the curator's well-intended warning but shook his head. He felt sure he was on the right track, and he had no intentions of quitting. A physician friend, who also learned of the experiment, even threatened to enter court proceedings that would legally prevent Haast from committing suicide.

It was during this period that he ran into financial difficulty. He had staked his entire savings on the premise that he could make his operation self-sustaining by supplying venom to the medical world. Amortizing the initial cost, day-by-day operation expenses and the cost of keeping a fresh supply of cobras coming in was causing a serious drain on his dwindling bank account. Although there was a ready market in the medical world for high-quality snake venom, the rewards were not commensurate with the production cost.

In something amounting to a blue funk, Haast stood in front of his laboratory one day and watched the steady flow of northbound and southbound traffic zip along U. S. 1—countless thousands of tourists hurrying along the highway looking for something to attract their interest before they returned home to New York, Kansas, or wherever they were from. Maybe, he thought, a few of them might be interested in seeing venom being extracted from big and deadly snakes such as cobras. He had a sign printed and by the time it was erected car after car began nosing into the parking ramp in front of his laboratory. Not only did curious people gladly pay an admission fee to watch a man pick up a venomous snake, but they clicked their cameras and went away thrilled by what they had seen and interested enough to tell others. All at once William Haast and his wife Clarita were in show business, at least on a part-time basis. His main interest was still the production of venom for the medical world.

Eleven months after launching his program of self-immunization, a cobra bit Haast. The snake was of medium size and the amount of injected venom was not great. It was, however, enough to bring swift death to the average human. The moment of truth was suddenly at hand. He could either yield to the urgings of his wife and seek medical aid or hold steady and see if his theory was sound.

In the hours that followed the bite, Haast had reason to doubt his stubbornness. An almost unbearable headache developed, and searing and burning pains wracked his entire body. But when the pain gradually dissipated and he was once more ready for work, he knew he had proved his point, and when he received his next bite his confidence in his immunity helped him through the ordeal with less agony.

Medical science has made many uses of cobra venom. Shortly before the announcement of the polio vaccine de-

veloped by Dr. Jonas Salk, researchers at the University of
Miami were enthusiastic over preliminary experiments in
their search for a cure for this dread disease. The neurotoxic
properties of cobra venom attack the motor cells of the central nervous system in much the same way that the polio
virus cripples and kills its victims.

That this project failed to provide the key to the cure of
polio has not in any way diminished the importance of the
cobra venom to the human race. In current production it is a
pain killer marketed under the brand name of Cobroxin and
has proved to be of inestimable value in alleviating the pain
of victims suffering from cancer and other serious diseases.

When he failed to die from his program of self-immunization, as prognosticated, and when he proved that he could
survive the bites of cobras that would kill the average human, the medical world began to take increasing interest in
William Haast. Tests were made and it was found that his
blood had itself become a serum so powerful that a transfusion might save the life of another victim of cobra bite.
The first big test came in 1956 when a boy was bitten by a
cobra in New Orleans while attending a snake show. Doctors sent a hurried call to Haast and a U. S. Marine Corps
jet fighter transported him to New Orleans in one hour and
fifteen minutes. A transfusion of his blood to the body of the
victim resulted in complete and swift recovery. This dona-
tion is only one of many such transfusions since, and although the offers of rewards have been many, Haast has
never accepted pay.

Haast and doctors who had watched him turn himself into
a human guinea pig pondered his maximum immunity to
cobra venom. He had survived thirty-three cobra bites, and
they were sure his tolerance was exceedingly high, since a
small fraction of a drop is generally sufficient to kill the

average man. But, they reasoned, there must somewhere be
an ultimate, a point of no return, when enough venom was
injected into his blood.

The answer to this question came one Sunday afternoon
in August of 1962. The usual tourist crowd had gathered to
watch Haast extract venom from his cobras. In the compound with him was another man, a friend and professional photographer who wanted to snap some close-up shots
of the operation.

Haast decided to use one of his largest specimens, a king
cobra that measured fourteen feet in length, only four feet
shorter than the world's record, weighing in excess of twenty
pounds. Its venom delivering capacity could amount to more
than thirty drops in a single bite!

The crowd that surrounded the milking compound fretted
at the summer heat, and the photographer adjusted the set-
tings on his camera as Haast opened the king cobra's pen.
The huge snake slithered out into the sunlight, and there
were muffled gasps from the spectators as the cobra reared a
third of its anterior portion into a defensive stance. In anger
the king cobra spread its hood and the massive body began
to sway.

There was talk from the crowd and lots of oohs and aahs.
A fat tourist chewed on a cigar and chuckled nervously.
"These snake handlers don't have to worry because all of
their snakes have had their fangs *pulled*," he told those
around him. Haast did not hear them because he was concentrating on his reptilian foe. Before him was one of the
largest and most powerful venomous snakes in the world!

In India and other countries where cobras are in plentiful
supply, the snakes are often handled with instruments which
frequently injure them and cause their death. To avoid damaging his valuable imported specimens, Haast from the beginning has elected to handle them entirely with his hands,

resulting in a strange sort of battle that resembles a fencing match between reptile and man.

The procedure Haast has devised consists of extending his right hand and waving it rhythmically in front of the cobra's head while his left hand reaches around eventually to grasp the snake by the neck. At times less than six inches separate his face from the cobra's head. The secret is careful, almost ballet timing, always anticipating the snake's next move.

"From the moment I take the king out of the cage, he's irate," said Haast. "He rears up to his famous striking stance, his hood spreads out in anger, and his cold, bronze, lidless eyes follow every movement I make. I watch him with equal intensity; in fact, I've been told I never blink while matching the king stare for stare, thrust for thrust."

Day after day, year after year, Haast has as a rule been successful in outguessing and outfencing his reptilian foe. Generally there is a quick grab after a match that may last from three to twenty minutes, and as the fingers of his left hand close around the snake's neck there is a sudden convulsion of coils. Seconds later the fangs are being pressed through the rubber diaphram on the top of a flask, and droplets of clear venom can be seen oozing down the side of the glass container.

On that summer afternoon, however, Haast allowed himself to be caught off-guard for a fleeting second, and in that brief interval the cobra lashed out. Its fangs sank into the dorsum of Haast's right index finger just forward of the knuckle. The force of the strike was so powerful that one of the fangs was broken from the snake's mouth. Haast sensed instantly that he had received his greatest dose of venom—and this time from a giant king cobra! His wife screamed as she noticed large beads of blood well up on her husband's finger. Few of the spectators even saw the strike, and most of those who noticed the blood thought it was just part of the act.

Calmly, Haast caught the cobra, removed the dangling fang, and went through the procedure of extracting the venom from the remaining fang. Finished, he returned the fourteen-foot cobra to its cage and walked from the extraction area. With the exception of Haast's wife, few of the spectators knew they had just witnessed a man receive a huge, and what should have been a lethal, dose of cobra venom.

At his wife's insistence, Haast agreed to go to the hospital, although he was experiencing none of the familiar symptoms, such as a sore throat, heavy eyelids, and general weakness. So devoid was he of these common symptoms that he insisted on storing the venom collected that afternoon and tidying up the laboratory. Haast's account of the events that followed in the next twenty-four hours, along with his personal feelings are recorded below: *

. . . On the way [to the hospital] I was devoid of symptoms, except for a swelling around the bite. Even after we got to the hospital, I felt as if nothing would happen. Several times I hopped out of bed and did calisthenics to prove the absence of paralysis.

Suddenly, however, my wife and my friend, [the photographer] noticed that my face had turned gray and that my lips had lost all color. Although I was feeling fine, I told them to order the first injection of antivenin. Luckily, just then Dr. Ben J. Sheppard arrived. He is a polio expert who has treated me often. Oddly enough his specialty is not unrelated to snake bites. Both bulbar polio and cobra venom kill by paralyzing nerve functions and eventually shutting off breathing. I had ended up in an iron lung after one of my cobra bites.

* Excerpt from an article by William Haast which appeared in *Family Weekly*, November 25, 1962.

Dr. Sheppard promptly took over and gave me my first antivenin shot. Then he checked my pulse, heart, and blood pressure. Everything was relatively normal and remained that way for the next 90 minutes.

I felt mildly elated. To anyone familiar with King Cobra venom, it was something of a phenomenon. Even Dr. Sheppard was amazed, but he was more cautious than I. Several times I told him I was ready to go home, and his answer was "Not so fast, young man." He was right.

Three hours after the bite, I felt a powerful sinking feeling, as if my bed, drifting on a cloud, had dramatically plunged into a huge chasm. Then, within seconds, the sensation reversed itself and I was rising rapidly. Simultaneously, I felt my abdomen tighten—and, grimacing with pain, I called out to Dr. Sheppard.

One look at me and he jumped from his chair. A check of my pulse, temperature, heart, and blood pressure showed they were all subnormal now. My skin was cold to the touch, and I began losing peripheral sensation in my body. My breathing grew increasingly rapid and shallow. I didn't know it then, but my heart was skipping beats, and I was in imminent danger of complete cardiac failure.

Everyone went into action. A hypodermic needle was plunged into my left leg, and to save time it was kept there, held fast by tape. Only the syringes were removed. One after another, they were filled with antivenin, then inserted into the needle in my leg and injected. At no time did I lose consciousness, and I never felt great pain; but there was a constant sensation of sinking lower and lower with each shallow breath.

It was then I asked permission to see my wife. I spoke briefly, telling her not to let the photographer feel guilty. His camera work at the scene was not responsible; I had made the mistake. I also talked about what my wife should do with the Serpentarium. At this, she burst into tears and ran from the room sobbing: "Bill's dying. He's dying."

Dr. Sheppard continued checking my heart and blood

pressure every few minutes. At one point, he could not get a pulse; my systolic pressure had fallen to 80 and my diastolic pressure was zero. My entire neurocirculatory system was rapidly collapsing.

At 11 o'clock that night, Dr. Sheppard was about ready to put me in an iron lung when, just as suddenly as I had "fallen" into the chasm, my blood pressure began to pick up. A half hour later, I felt I could have walked out of the hospital. At 1:30 A.M. Dr. Sheppard announced I would recover.

The next afternoon I was back at the Serpentarium. Dr. Sheppard wanted me to stay in the hospital at least another day, but I insisted on leaving.

The following Sunday afternoon, I successfully extracted venom from the same King Cobra that bit me. The "rematch" proved momentarily too much for my wife; after the King made a powerful but unsuccessful strike at me, Clarita ran sobbing from the scene.

Now that I have survived a King Cobra bite, I am convinced that my human guinea-pig experiment has paid off. I don't believe a cobra can ever kill me. . . .

Since recovering from the bite of the king cobra in the summer of 1962, William Haast has been bitten by a number of other poisonous snakes, but none have proved nearly so serious. According to Haast his immunity also brought him through the bite of the blue krait, the only person in the world to recover spontaneously from this snake's bite.

The Haast laboratory supplies venom from any type of poisonous snake found in all parts of the world, but his chief interest still lies in the cobra. Cobras, as with many other snakes in captivity, refuse to eat, so Haast has devised a formula and a method of force-feeding. The formula is basically a high-protein concoction closely simulating the food on which a cobra in the wild state would subsist. It is fed to the snake by means of a plastic tube inserted through the mouth and into the stomach and forced down by a special type of gun resembling a caulking gun. This special diet keeps the snakes healthy, thus providing them with the necessary body energy to produce a uniform venom supply each time they are "milked."

With the establishment of his Serpentarium in 1948, Haast's career has made him a worldwide medical wonder. By successfully self-immunizing himself with cobra venom his blood has become a valuable serum. As early as 1949 he had 500 cc. of his blood processed by a blood bank to be used as an anticoral snakebite serum in case of emergency envenomation treatment in the state of Florida. This was the first specific antivenin in the entire country.

In 1953 his own human serum saved the life of a cobra bite victim in Hollywood, Florida. A year later he gave serum to a coral snakebite victim at Miami Beach and to another in West Palm Beach. Both victims survived. His blood serum was also given to save the life of a victim of a black widow spider bite in Miami.

In 1955 his Serpentarium processed the first coral snake serum from rabbits with the use of cobra venom. And in 1961 Haast produced the first radioactive cobra venom for physiological tracings in an effort to help the chemist discover the action of venom on a living animal.

For Haast, the basic reason for his Serpentarium's existence has finally been recognized. Venom is now being used in chemistry and biochemistry for a source of valuable enzymes. Through his efforts it has been proved that snake venom has a useful purpose and can benefit mankind through science.*

* A biography of William Haast, *Cobras in His Garden* by Harry Kursh, has been published by Harvey House, Inc.

9

COLLECTION

Anyone interested in herpetology is drawn almost magnetically to a cage containing a live snake. It is here one may study a creature frequently seen for only a fleeting moment in the wilds. The confines of the cage permit the observer to watch closely the fluidlike movement of the body as the snake prowls about the rocks and branches and to see the nervous flicking in and out of the sensitive tongue.

If the snake is one's personal pet that must be cared for day after day for months or even years, the interest is heightened tenfold. During this time the naturalist is presented with the opportunity of watching so much more than could ever be seen by daily trips to a zoo. Shedding, for example, is something that visitors to the zoo and those who stroll through the woods can see only in part. A snake does not simply wriggle out of its old skin like someone pulling off a sweater. At times the process may last for many hours. To watch a snake capture and swallow a live mouse is admittedly not a performance that will appeal to everyone, but to a naturalist it is a fascinating, complicated, and necessary operation that must be seen to be fully understood.

In many ways, a caged snake is one of the most easily cared for pets, but there are certain rules that must be observed if both snake and owner are to derive the greatest benefits from the association.

I was about eleven years old and probably under the influence of Frank "Bring 'em Back Alive" Buck when I became lured to the game of capturing and keeping snakes. Until then there had always been the normal youngster's collection of pets about the house—a dog, a cat, a bowl of goldfish, and an occasional rabbit.

Then came that magical spring. The bare branches of the oaks, sycamores, and sweetgums, which had for so long stood stark and ugly against a leaden gray sky, seemed to burst forth in greenery. White petals of flowering dogwood unfolded to compete with the patches of snow left over from winter, as the warm mantle of spring spread over the Virginia countryside. Nature was coming back to life, and she beckoned a boy to run through her woods and throw rocks and swing on vines and be amazed at all of the newness around him.

I fretted through the weekly five-day stint of confinement in the schoolroom, but the sun was coming up earlier each morning and the afternoons were growing increasingly longer. And then would come Saturday—a day which I think God must have set aside exclusively for youngsters. It was a day to slip out of the house at dawn and devour countless hours of freedom before being corralled for such mundane tasks as taking a bath, getting a haircut or studying the Sunday School lesson. It was on one of these early spring Saturdays that I caught my first snake—a fourteen-inch ribbon snake which I took home and put in a large zinc tub. He was either exceedingly hungry or well conditioned for captivity, for when I tossed a few earthworms in the tub he ate them without hesitation.

During the remainder of that spring and throughout the summer that followed I scoured the surrounding woods and explored every nook and cranny in the bed of the creek that meandered through the valley. Tolerant, though sometimes reluctant, parents accepted my ever growing menagerie of box turtles, toads, crayfish, lizards, and snakes. As the summer wore on I was kept busy building cages for my collection, which by August included a foundling screech owl, two flying squirrels, a crow, and an assortment of other creatures that hopped, creeped, and crawled.

The biggest problem, as my embryonic zoo grew, was keeping the inhabitants fed. The water snakes would eat every minnow and frog I could dip up from the creek, and the owl liked fish and bits of ground beef. The box turtles, twenty-seven of them, feasted on cantaloupe rinds, and I industriously chased insects and dug earthworms for snakes and water turtles. The flying squirrels and the crow, cheerful mendicants that they were, seemed to revel in their captivity and the free board it offered. They were happy to eat almost anything I put in their cages, from popcorn to leftovers from the table.

I learned that summer that a zookeeper can have too many charges, and before September had chilled into autumn I began to release my menagerie. I had come to look on myself more as a harassed jailer than a student of nature.

The little screech owl was the first to go. When I had found it, it had been a tiny ball of gray fluff lying helpless on the ground beside a fallen tree. That had been in the month of May, and by September it was in full feather and had learned to lift its little *ears* and complain to the moon in its lonely tremulous wail. One evening with the setting sun I took it out of its cage and lofted it over my head. It spread its wings and sailed away into the gathering gloom.

It came back the next evening and continued these visits for nearly a week, and then it was gone for good.

After the owl the liberation progressed swiftly. Tadpoles that had shed their tails and turned into frogs were dumped back into the creek. Snakes were carried far back into the woods and released, and turtles were returned to the ponds from which they had been captured. My zoo rapidly became a ghost town of empty boxes, cages, and wire enclosures. It was during this repatriation that I made an interesting discovery, and it is something I have never forgotten. While it is fun to capture wild things, it is equally as exciting to release them. The stodgy old box turtle would sit still for a moment, safely enclosed in its shell, and then gradually it would lower the anterior portion of its plastron like the ramp coming down on a landing barge, and its head would ease out for a look at its new surroundings. Then slowly it would begin to plod off toward a thicket of blackberry brambles, doubtless wondering—if turtles wonder—why it had been captured in the first place and, further, why it was being released unharmed after several months of imprisonment.

One amusing incident occurred while I was liberating my woodland pets. In early summer I had captured a beautiful specimen of a four-foot black racer near an outcropping of granite boulders. Ready now to set it free, I placed it in a cloth bag and returned it to the same general area. When I emptied it out on the ground it slithered up on a fallen tree and sampled the air with darting tongue and viewed the surroundings to be sure that it was actually free. Then it glided off toward a pile of rocks.

I turned and started walking away, but before I had gone twenty steps I chanced to glance over my shoulder and was surprised to see the racer coming toward me. I stopped and waited to find out what it was going to do. When it caught up with me it crawled between my feet and lay motionless. I reached down and carefully picked it up and returned it to the fallen tree. Once again I started to leave, and as before the snake began to follow me. Walking rapidly I stopped again when I had covered about twenty-five yards. The snake was still on my trail. Once more I carried it back to the log, and this time I broke into a full run and did not stop until I reached my bicycle parked on a dirt road nearly a quarter of a mile away.

Since that time I have often wondered about the incident, and I wish I had taken more time to see how long the snake would have continued to follow me. I can only conclude that either it had not wanted to be released in the area where it had been captured, or maybe it had developed a liking for me and decided that captivity was not so bad after all.

Oddly enough that was not the only time I have had a snake follow me, and odder still, on the second occasion the snake was also a black racer. This time, nearly five years later, two friends and I were on a summer camping trip in the Blue Ridge Mountains. Early one morning just about sunrise we were hiking along the famed Appalachian Trail and found a black racer twined through the branches of a limb that had broken off a dead tree. The temperature was in the low fifties, and the snake was almost stiff with the cold. I picked up the branch with the snake still entwined and carried it along for a mile or so. With the rising sun the air warmed rapidly and gradually the snake began to move.

Placing the branch on the ground my friends and I sat down for a brief rest and watched as the snake unlimbered in a patch of sunshine. When we started walking again the snake began to follow us. We would run for a way, but when we stopped it would invariably catch up with us. Once we made a detour off from the trail and waited in a small clearing. When it caught up with us at that point we were convinced that it was not simply following the trail. All told, I suppose it followed us for at least half a mile.

I have no answer for the unusual behavior of either snake. I do not believe black racers and I have some kind of strange affinity for one another because I have caught numerous specimens since and some have been considerably less friendly. One large racer caught in Florida bit me so viciously on the right hand when I attempted to pick it up that I had to use tweezers to remove two of its teeth that broke off in my flesh.

Over the years since that summer of my short-lived zoo, I have collected and studied many types of wildlife, but I believe snakes in general have presented the greatest challenge. If one wishes to trap and keep a crow or an opossum for a pet, it can be done with little or no experience. All that is needed is the proper equipment and a little luck. If caught young, both bird and marsupial are docile and easy to care for, since they will thrive on most any kinds of food humans or their domestic pets enjoy.

The amateur herpetologist who strolls through the woods and picks up an occasional box turtle or plucks an anole from a vine or catches a horned lizard has little or nothing to worry about. As with the crow and the opossum, turtles and lizards are simple to care for.

Snakes, on the other hand, are neither easy to catch nor easy to feed, and unless the collector is something of an expert, he stands a chance of being seriously injured should he make an ill-advised grab.

Most snakes in the United States are harmless, but one mistake can be one too many. It therefore behooves the collector to exercise caution when attempting to catch any snake. All must be handled with care if they are to be captured uninjured.

The time-honored forked stick used to pin the snake's neck to the ground until he can be safely clutched behind the head is unquestionably an effective means of restraint. Unless it is used with extreme care, however, the cervical ribs will be broken, eventually causing the snake's death.

Far better than the forked stick is a tool known as a snake stick. It consists of a length of wood approximately the size of a broom handle. A length of iron about as big around as a pencil and bent in the shape of a U is fitted horizontally to the end of the stick. A companion tool used with the snake stick is a bag hung open-mouthed on a metal hoop attached to the end of a stick and resembling a fisherman's landing net.

When a desirable specimen is spotted, the collector slides the U-shaped hook under the snake and lifts it into the bag. In this manner the snake is not injured, and if the bag is deep enough it is unable to escape. The next step is to transfer the catch into a suitable carrying container. Closely woven sacks are ideal, and they should be secured at the top with a length of cord. Bags are much more suitable for holding freshly captured snakes than are boxes, since the snake is unable to damage itself by striking at the solid walls. Even a large and vicious rattler is virtually harmless in a bag. But, here a note of warning might well be sounded. A snake can strike through a cloth bag.

A professional snake catcher near Jacksonville, Florida, died recently as a result of being careless with a bagful of snakes. He had spent the day in a wooded area, and during this time he had captured about a dozen rattlers of medium size. The following day he was found dead beside a railroad track. It was first thought that he had been hit by a train or perhaps had died of natural causes. When an autopsy was performed, however, two fang marks were found near the base of his neck on the right side. It is logical to assume that after his day in the woods the collector climbed up to the railroad right-of-way and slung the bag of snakes over his shoulder as he began his homeward trek. One of the snakes feeling the body heat probably struck blindly, its fangs penetrating the bag and sinking into the man's neck.

A bag containing a poisonous snake should be carried by the top and well away from the body.

Newcomers to the game of catching snakes and those still too squeamish or cautious to pick up a small harmless snake with bare hands will find that a pair of forceps such as are used in the kitchen will be useful. Care should be exercised to avoid squeezing the snake too tightly.

Once home with the captive snakes they may be safely contained in a wooden box with a close-fitting screen wire top. If kept outdoors the box should be in a shaded area, since snakes can be killed by the direct rays of hot summer sun.

Snakes, like all reptiles, are cold-blooded, and with rare exceptions their body temperature coincides with the surrounding atmosphere. In the direct rays of the sun, however, radiated and reflected heat may bring about insolation above their body tolerance, and death may occur in less than a quarter of an hour.

Unless the amateur collector has adequate quarters for his snakes he should be content to keep them captive for only short periods and then return them to their natural environments—with the exception of the poisonous varieties. Some students of nature will doubtless disagree, but I believe any dangerous snake should be humanely destroyed whenever encountered. It is true that rattlesnakes, water moccasins, and others of their kind are beneficial to some extent where mankind's well-being is concerned, but their potential danger outweighs their value. To release a poisonous snake is, to my way of thinking, tantamount to leaving a loaded and cocked gun in a place where it may be picked up by the unwary.

Some snakes make better pets than others. The two North American species which records have proved to be the best are the indigo (*Drymarchon corais*) and hog-nosed (*Heterodon*) snakes. Runners-up are rat snakes and ribbon snakes. Pit vipers seldom thrive in captivity for long periods of time.

Those interested in keeping captive snakes should give some study to the construction of a terrarium that can provide a suitable home. I have found that a cage about a foot longer than the occupant is ideal. Such dimensions enable the snake to move about with some degree of freedom and affords the observer the chance to see his pet in surroundings that can be made to simulate natural conditions.

The floor of the cage should be of natural wood or plywood. Glass should never be used because it is difficult for a snake to move on a completely smooth surface. Three of the sides may be made of wood, with a glass front panel to permit viewing. Screen wire should not be used because all but the most lethargic snakes will spend much of their time searching for a way out, and continued nosing and pushing against the screen will abrade the head and frequently result in serious infection.

For the average-size snake the top of the cage should be hinged and made of fine-mesh hardware cloth. All snakes are exceedingly adept at the art of escaping through small openings. The lid should fit tightly and be secured with a hook.

Freshly caught snakes of almost any species will more quickly come to accept captivity if they are provided with some hiding spot in which they can *hole up* for a few days. This need be only a small box similar to a bird house in a corner of the cage. As time passes the snake will grow bolder and eventually leave its solitary retreat.

The most interesting type of terrarium is the one that closely simulates the natural surroundings from which the snake has been taken. This is possible by adding some rocks, sand, and branches as well as the imagination of the keeper.

Snakes to be kept through the winter months may be permitted to hibernate if the temperature in the cage drops below sixty degrees Fahrenheit. The temperature should never be allowed to go below forty degrees or the snake will die. In normal hibernation snakes remain dormant for four or five months and require no food or water. If, however, they are to be kept *awake* around the calendar, then food and water are just as necessary in January as in July. No tropical snake ever hibernates, although some aestivate in periods of intense heat, but those held in captivity in temperate zones will not resort to this practice.

It is important that snake cages be maintained in a dry condition. This holds true for even the amphibious specimens such as the water moccasins, common water snakes, and swamp snakes. If water dishes are large enough to permit it, many snakes will spend their entire time partly submerged, and this will soon lead to skin trouble. In the wilds water snakes spend most of their time in branches or out on the ground. In captivity they tend to reverse this procedure if permitted, since water is a natural hiding place for them.

The only time a moist condition may be called for is when a snake is shedding. When the keeper notes the loosening of the epidermis of his captive specimen he should keep close check, and should the snake seem to be having difficulty it should be placed in a damp cotton bag and allowed to remain overnight. This will loosen the skin to an extent that the shedding may be accomplished more easily.

The serious collector will occasionally find himself far removed from civilization when he captures a valuable specimen. If the snake cannot be kept alive it should be quickly

killed and the body transported to safekeeping as soon as possible. For identification and future study the weight, length,
and markings are the three most important points to be
noted.

Once while exploring the headwaters of a Florida stream
I killed a giant rattler that measured well over six feet in
length. After I had put a .22 bullet through the reptile's
neck I noticed a large bulge near its midsection. I was two
days away from civilization, so I placed the dead snake in a
gunnysack for later examination. The heat of midsummer
and the excessive humidity worked quickly, and by the following day the snake was a putrid mass too foul-smelling
to keep in the boat. I never learned what the snake had
swallowed, though I suspect it was a large marsh rabbit.

The collector who finds himself in a similar situation
would be wise to skin the snake, leaving the head and tail
attached. It should be rolled loosely and either tanned or
placed in a preservative as soon as possible.

Freshly killed specimens can be well preserved if im-
mersed in Formalin. Snakes which are bulged with freshly
swallowed prey should have the stomach contents removed.
A hypodermic syringe is a valuable tool for the collector. He
can use it to inject Formalin into the body cavities without
damaging the outward appearance.

As civilization spreads and wildlife of all kinds becomes
increasingly scarce, many people are resorting more and
more to the use of a camera to "collect" specimens. In several
respects a good, clear color slide of a living snake can be far
more interesting than a specimen pickled in a container of
formaldehyde.

Wildlife photography, and especially detailed color photography, demands exact lighting and proper background if
the subject is to be used for study. Getting good pictures of
birds and animals that spend most of their time in the open

can be time-consuming and often exasperating. The job is next to impossible when the subjects are snakes. From the boldest mamba of Africa to the shyest coral of the western hemisphere, all snakes spend most of their time in places where they are least likely to be observed and consequently present the poorest targets for the camera. The result is that most detailed pictures of snakes are taken on panes of ground glass with no natural surroundings at all.

Some years ago I had an assignment from a magazine to get color pictures of all poisonous snakes in North America, and the contract called for them to be pictured in their natural environment.

Upon undertaking the assignment I envisioned a few weeks of woodland travel throughout the southern states— a vacation in the spring of the year. My wife and I had a vacation all right, and it was one of the most unusual we have ever taken.

For the first week we made numerous fruitless treks into first one swamp and then another and hiked over countless miles of countryside with local guides who were positive they could lead us to rattlesnake dens and water moccasin ponds. In some cases we found snakes and occasionally in abundance, but by and large the lighting and the background were never conducive to good clear photography.

After a hundred or more color and black and white photographs had been processed and studied, I came to the conclusion that I would have to adopt a different procedure if I was to present the editor with a set of sparkling pictures that would show the snakes in "their natural setting." It would be necessary to capture the snakes I needed and transport them to places where lighting and background would be compatible.

Thus began our snake catching and photographing safari that led us through Alabama, Georgia, and down into Florida. After a stopover at Ross Allen's Reptile Institute at Silver Springs we continued south toward the Everglades Wonder Gardens at Bonito Springs, where we had an appointment to invade the Big Cypress Swamp with Wilbur Piper.

By the time we reached Tampa many pictures had been taken and scores of snakes had been collected. The snakes were in several cloth bags which I had placed on the rear seat of the car. We considered taking a motel for the night, but I wanted to be on hand at Bonito Springs early the next morning so we elected to keep driving.

It was Friday night and the traffic on U. S. 41 was particularly heavy. We stopped at Bradenton for dinner, hoping the traffic would ease off, but it was just as bad when we again started to roll. The rainy season of early spring had just ended, and the highway was flanked by water-filled ditches. I wondered what a person would do if he had to stop and change a tire.

After an hour or so on the road I suggested that Dorothy pour us a couple of cups of coffee from the Thermos in a basket behind the front seat. She took the flashlight from the glove compartment and a moment later I heard her make a funny little noise in her throat. Glancing over at her I asked what was the matter.

"The snakes," she said. "They are all out of the bags!"

My first thought was that she was just attempting to make a joke, predicated on the fact that she had been strongly opposed to keeping the collection on the back seat instead of in the trunk. I had worked long and hard catching them, and I did not want to risk asphyxiating them with carbon monoxide gas that might filter into the close confines of the trunk. As a result I had separated the snakes into the three large cloth bags. One contained about half a dozen rattlers, the other nearly a dozen copperheads and water moccasins.

The third bag was filled with an assortment of colorful, but nonpoisonous snakes. I had tied the top of the bags with a common cord and knotted it with a simple bow knot.

"I'm serious." Dorothy said, a note of alarm in her voice. "The bags are empty!"

Chancing a quick glance over my right shoulder I saw by the flashlight beam that she was indeed serious. The bags *were* empty and that meant the snakes were loose in the car.

"Get your feet up on the seat and sit still," I said, trying to recall the construction of the car.

All too clearly I could remember the space under the front seat that led to the back. I had many times passed the vacuum cleaner hose completely under the seat.

I considered hitting the brake and skidding off onto the grassy shoulder, but it was narrow and uncertain at best, and we might turn over in the water-filled ditch. Desperately I longed to see the glow of a neon-lighted service station, but the road ahead was black except for the oncoming glare of headlights. I wondered how long the snakes had been out of the bags. I had checked them as we left the restaurant and the knot was secure then, but now there could be no doubt that no less than eighteen poisonous snakes were loose in the car. Any of that number might right at that moment be foraging about over the front floorboards and around my feet as they searched for some route of escape. They were wild and dangerous creatures, and I knew that any sudden movement on my part might cause one of them to strike.

Slowly, I relaxed the pressure on the accelerator pedal, and the car slowed to twenty-five miles per hour. In the rear view mirror I caught sight of an overtaking car coming up fast. The driver blinked his lights indicating his desire to pass. Oncoming traffic penned him down behind my rear bumper as he waited for an opening. He expressed his irritation at my reduced speed by several long blasts on his horn.

I could guess he was muttering some derogatory remarks about drivers who poke along at a snail's pace in the middle of the night. I did not blame him, but at the moment I could not concern myself with his anger. All I wanted was to find some escape from the predicament into which I had unwittingly thrust my wife and myself.

Ahead, several hundred yards, I could see a tiny glow of red light. As we drew near it resolved into a reflector of the type used to mark a side road. It was the first turnoff since we had discovered the empty bags, and I had no intention of missing it. The fingers of my left hand flicked the turn indicator, and I hoped the agitated driver behind me would notice my intentions.

Both feet still motionless on the floor, I gave the wheel a sharp right turn, and the car left the highway and nosed into the dirt road that led back into the swamps. When we had traveled fifty feet I stepped down hard on the brake pedal and turned off the ignition switch.

"Get out and run around to the front of the car!" I ordered, opening my door.

The next instant we were both standing in the glare of the headlights and feeling as if we had escaped a mobile snake pit. Beneath our feet was solid ground, and the harsh headlights flooded the swamp and cast inky black shadows behind us and from the trees that flanked the road.

Back on the highway there was the monotonous swish of northbound and southbound cars. In the intervals of silence there were two other important sounds. One was the buzz of rattlers and the other was the singing of mosquitoes. The rainy spring had provided ample breeding places and countless hundreds of hungry mosquitoes were vectoring in on the two human targets that stood in the headlight glare.

Alternately wiping first one arm and then the other and slapping at the back of my neck, I listened for the sounds of the irate rattlers to cease. Now and then, when the highway traffic was momentarily quiet, we could hear a heavy serpent body drop out of the car and onto the road.

In her excitement to get out of the car Dorothy had dropped the flashlight. I told her not to worry, adding that I was sure we would be able to find it when we were ready to leave. Immediately after our escape from the snake-infested car we were both thoroughly content just to stand in the headlight glare, but when fifteen minutes had passed and we had been peppered by countless mosquitoes, we both began to long for the bottle of insect repellent in the glove compartment.

Twice I started to walk around to the right side of the car and look for the flashlight, but both times I was turned back by the warning buzz of a rattler that had dropped to the ground but had not yet decided to leave the scene.

When we could stand the mosquitoes no longer I tied my handkerchief to the end of a short stick and set the cloth ablaze with the flame from my cigarette lighter. It was a primitive and short-lived torch, but it did serve to guide me to the flashlight, which I found on the ground close beside the right front door. Snatching it up I flicked the switch and tossed the burning handkerchief aside.

What was needed most at the moment was the bottle of insect repellent. With the light, I made an inspection of the front seat and floorboards. When I found that area clear I quickly dug the bottle out of the glove compartment and hurried back around to the front of the car.

For the next couple of minutes we busied ourselves by lavishly smearing the repellent on our arms and faces. The mosquitoes still sung around our ears, but their feast was over and the relief was welcome.

After carefully scanning the ground ahead of us and seeing no snakes we began to inspect the interior of the car. All of the cloth bags on the back seat were empty, but coiled loosely on top of them was a pert little four-lined chicken snake. The harmless creature with its bright yellow body and dark longitudinal stripes apparently had not found captivity as distasteful as his fellow prisoners and had not joined the exodus.

Before we could feel safe about getting back into the car and continuing our journey that night, however, every piece of luggage had to be removed and the interior of the car searched carefully. Except for the chicken snake all of the others had departed. When Dorothy finally agreed there were no more snakes still lurking inside, we climbed back in and continued on to Bonito Springs.

Fortunately most of the needed photographs had already been taken, and the few we still wanted were easy to get with the help of Bill Piper, who had an abundance of fine specimens in his cages. The trip back into the Big Cypress Swamp with Piper as our guide proved a naturalist's treat and was a fitting climax to the snake assignment.

10

SNAKEBITE

The incidence of poisonous snakebite in North America is relatively very low when compared to many other parts of the world. Any bite, however, is potentially a serious one, and prompt first aid and proper subsequent medical care are of extreme importance. In this country the highest death rates from snakebite are reported from Arizona, Florida, Georgia, Alabama, South Carolina, and Texas, in this order.

In North America there are basically only four types of deadly poisonous snakes. These are the rattlers, water moccasins, copperheads, and coral snakes. The first three are pit vipers of the family Crotalidae, and their venom is primarily hemotoxic in nature, attacking and destroying the red blood cells. The venom of the coral snakes, of the family Elapidae, is neurotoxic and almost purely paralytic in its action. Because of the difference in the treatment of these two types of snakebites, the coral snake will be discussed later in this chapter.

The first and most important consideration for anyone bitten by a snake is to determine what kind has been encountered. Knowing the type of snake is important so that proper treatment may be begun. Admittedly, this admonition is at times easier to issue than to follow, because on-the-spot identification is often difficult when the snake is seen for only a fleeting moment. This is true sometime even for a trained ophiologist.

There are certain basic guides that anyone can follow in making this important identification. The rattlesnakes, which are responsible for most of the serious snakebites in North America, are the easiest because of the rattles at the tip of their tails. It should be noted, however, that there are occasions when the string of rattles may be broken off due to some accident. All of the pit vipers—the rattlers, copperheads, and water moccasins—have wedge-shaped heads which are considerably larger than the neck. With a few exceptions nonvenomous snakes have heads that are about the size of, or only a little larger than, the necks.

A second, but less reliable, key to the type of snake are factors concerning the bite. All snakes are wild animals, and all will bite if they feel they are in danger of being trapped or injured. Nonpoisonous snakes generally leave a U-shaped mark where the teeth have broken the skin. The pain is as slight as so many briar scratches. The crotalids, or pit vipers, have two movable fangs that are normally encased in sheaths in the roof of the mouth and erected only at the moment of the strike. Classically, the marks left by the bite of these poisonous snakes are two punctures. In severe cases there will be intense pain and rapid local swelling. Early constitutional symptoms will be weakness, vertigo, numbness, and a tingling sensation about the lips. Occasionally a poisonous snake will leave only one fang puncture, since it may have recently lost one of its fangs or the angle of the bite was such that only one of the fangs entered the flesh.

The severity of the bite depends on several factors. One is the toxicity of the venom. It does not always follow that a large snake is more dangerous than a smaller one of the same species. For that matter, toxicity of venom from snakes of equal size often varies considerably. Other factors concern the location of the bite on the victim, the depth of penetration of the fangs, as well as the victim's general physical and psychological condition. A fine specimen of a two-hundred-pound man may have a morbid dread of snakes in general and thus suffer far more serious complications than a ninety-pound boy who, through ignorance, considers a snakebite to be no more serious than a skinned knee.

If fang punctures, swelling, and other symptoms are present it is reasonable to assume that the snake was a pit viper, and first aid treatment should be begun with the shortest possible delay.

Under ideal conditions a snakebite victim would immediately be immobilized and placed under medical care; preferably in a hospital. Since snakebites seldom occur on the lawn in front of a hospital, it is important that the potential victim know what to do until medical assistance can be secured.

Even before the arrival of early colonists, the American Indian had devised a method of snakebite treatment that is still today the most acceptable means of first aid. This consists of a tourniquet above the bite and removal of venom by suction. Such treatment is crude and often dangerous when administered by the untrained, but it has been responsible for saving so many lives that it has made a place for itself in the medical world.

The first consideration is the application of the tourniquet. This may be fashioned of anything from a shoelace to a length of surgical rubber tubing. Satisfactory tourniquets have been made of strips of cloth torn from a shirt and even a length of vine. The important point is that the tourniquet be placed above the bite and tightened to such a degree as to impede the flow of blood and venom through the veins and back to the heart.

On many occasions irreparable damage has been done when an overwrought snakebite victim and those attempting to assist him have applied a tourniquet and bound it so tightly around an arm or leg as to occlude arterial flow of blood. Such restrictive ligatures are effective in retarding the spread of venom, but should be used only if the extremity is to be later sacrificed by surgery to save the victim's life. Under average conditions a tourniquet need only be tight enough to impede the return flow of blood. It should be loosened for about a minute every ten to fifteen minutes.

Indians and early settlers found that after a moderately tight tourniquet was applied, incisions could be made over the fang punctures and much of the venom could be extracted by suction. The most logical and readily available *sucking device* was, and still is, the human mouth. In modern times, however, pharmaceutical houses have developed snakebite kits which include suction cups and vacuum syringes that are quite effective in the removal of venom. Studies have proved that as much as 50 percent of injected venom can be withdrawn in subcutaneous bites and those in which the fangs have penetrated only a slight distance below the skin. Generally speaking, less venom is withdrawn by suction when the fangs have penetrated deeply into the flesh.

It is of extreme importance that incision of the wound and suction be begun almost immediately after the bite if the most beneficial results are to be obtained. Experiments have proved that extended suction treatment is to little or no avail, since what poison there is to be recovered will be withdrawn in the first half hour.

Many investigators have been highly critical of the cut-and-suck method, contending that anyone other than a physician is quite likely to cause damage to underlying tendons and ligaments by the careless use of a pocketknife, scalpel, or razor blade. This objection is well founded and it should be emphasized that the incisions over the fang punctures be no more than a quarter of an inch in depth, even less when the bite is on a finger or toe.

In the early 1950's a small bombshell was exploded in the outdoor world when articles began to appear in newspapers and leading magazines concerning a new and radically different kind of treatment for snakebite.

No longer was it necessary to cut the flesh and suck out the venom. Instead, the articles stated, all the victim had to do was pack the bitten extremity—be it hand or foot—in ice and place a tourniquet above the bite. After that he could make his way to a hospital for proper medical treatment.

Since it was recognized that an adequate supply of ice was seldom available on hunting and fishing trips and other junkets into wilderness country where poisonous snakes were likely to be encountered, the promoters of this new form of treatment advised the outdoorsman to equip himself with one or more bottles of ethyl chloride, which is a compressed refrigerant occasionally used as a surface anesthetic. It was recommended that, in lieu of a supply of ice, the ethyl chloride be sprayed on the flesh around the vicinity of the bite just to the point of frost formation.

This form of snakebite treatment was known as the "L-C" method. The initials stood simply for the two elements. L was for ligature or tourniquet, and C was for cryotherapy, or treatment by refrigeration. The whole idea was based on the postulate, suggested as far back as 1906, that chilling the flesh around the point of bite would retard the movement and destructive action of the venom and permit the natural defense mechanism of the body gradually to neutralize the poison.

There are no records to prove how many victims of snakebite placed their faith in the "L-C" method of treatment, but it is an established fact that far greater harm than good was done. Later, and more thorough, investigation proved the original idea that refrigeration did markedly reduce the action of the venom locally, but there was no significant evidence that the body was able successfully to counteract venom which had been retarded by refrigeration. Regrettably, many physicians called upon to manage snakebite cases adopted the treatment, and much to their sorrow found that dependency on this *new* form of treatment often resulted in the necessity for amputation of an arm or leg. While artificial chilling served to retard the spread of venom, there was the inevitable *warm-up* period. Tissue that had been deprived of a steady flow of blood had *died!* The ultimate result was that the limb subjected to prolonged refrigeration frequently became gangrenous, and amputation was demanded if the victim's life was to be saved.

The only use to which ice is currently permissible by many physicians handling snakebite cases is when it is placed directly over the bite for short periods of time to relieve pain.

While many lives have been saved by the first aid measure of tourniquet and suction treatment, this alone is frequently not enough to prevent death when large doses of snake venom are received. Today, the possibility of recovery is greatly enhanced by what is known as *serotherapy*, or treatment of snakebite by the use of antivenin. Serotherapy is, in fact, the keystone of all treatment. Without it, recovery is largely on a hit-or-miss basis.

The history of the development of antivenin stretches back over a century, but not until recent years has it reached its state of near-perfection. Early attempts were to produce a vaccine that would render a person immune to snake venom in much the same manner as smallpox or other dreaded diseases could be prevented. Unsuccessful on this tack, the experimenters looked for a serum that would effectively neutralize venom *after* it had been injected into the bloodstream. In North America it was first believed that the venoms of a dozen or more different kinds of snakes had to be combined to produce an effective serum. One of the most significant recent developments is the discovery—largely attributed to Wyeth Laboratories, of Marietta, Pennsylvania—that a combination of only four venoms is necessary in the production of a serum that offers protection from the bites of all of the pit vipers found in North and South America, as well as certain other poisonous snakes found in other parts of the world.

To produce this antivenin the venoms of four species of snakes are used. These are the tropical rattler (*Crotalus terrificus*), the fer-de-lance (*Bothrops atrox*), the eastern diamondback rattler (*Crotalus adamanteus*), and the Texas rattler (*Crotalus atrox*).

The combined venoms are administered in gradually increasing doses to large specimens of horses that are in excellent health. When these horses reach a satisfactory state of immunization, they are bled and the blood is subjected to various chemical processes that separate the serum. This serum is then sterilized and cleansed of impurities and finally evaporated until only a small amount of white powder remains. This dehydrated serum is vacuum packed in vials. When ready to be used it is dissolved in distilled water and injected into the snakebite victim with a hypodermic syringe. Antivenin kits, complete with disposable syringes, are available at drugstores, and the dried antivenin will remain potent for at least five years without refrigeration and at outdoor temperatures such as would be experienced on extended field trips.

It has been generally acknowledged by modern investigators that serotherapy or the administration of antivenin is the keystone in the treatment of all bites by crotalid snakes. It is not, however, a magic cure-all or a simple panacea to be used indiscriminately by those untrained in medicine. Antivenin is a heterologous serum, and as such, appropriate measures must be taken to rule out the presence of dangerous sensitivity on the part of the patient. A skin test should be made by the injection of a small amount of the antivenin. If the test proves negative—the patient shows no adverse effects—the initial dose can be administered.

It has been found that a large initial dose is more effective in counteracting venom than several divided doses of the same amount. It was once believed that small portions of the antivenin should be injected in the vicinity of the bite. More recent investigation has proven, however, that the local swelling generally surrounding the bitten area retards absorption of the antivenin and its injection only increases the edema. Under no conditions should serum ever be injected into a finger or toe.

Snakebite in children often presents a more acute problem than a bite of the same severity suffered by an adult. The reason is that children generally have less resistance and less body fluids with which to dilute the venom. Because of this, children may require twice the dosage of serum that suffices for adults.

It should be remembered that as long as a snakebite victim still lives it is never too late to administer serum. Injections of large doses given when a patient was apparently dying have resulted in recovery.

There are only two genera of coral snakes found in the United States. Their range is confined to the southern states from the Carolinas south throughout Florida and westward to Arizona. With rare exceptions, coral snakes have distinctive markings which are readily identifiable. The tip of the nose is jet black, followed immediately by a bright yellow band which encircles the head. Behind this is a broad black band encircling the neck. The length of the body is a series of broad black and red bands, and each of these is separated by narrow yellow bands.

The size of the average adult coral snake is about 30 inches in length with the official record at 47½ inches. They are slender snakes with the head no larger than the neck. Unlike the elliptical or cat eyes of the pit vipers, the coral snakes have eyes with round pupils. They are oviparous, depositing several eggs in early summer which hatch about ten weeks later.

Coral snakes differ significantly from the pit vipers in numerous ways. Most important is the type of venom they possess and their method of injecting it into their victims. Unlike the large movable fangs of the crotalids, the corals possess two small fixed fangs in the front of the upper jaw. Instead of the hypodermiclike fangs of the pit vipers, those of the corals are solid, and the venom flows down the surface from ducts at the base of each fang.

Coral snakes do not strike. Instead, they bite, and once they have closed their jaws on their victim they chew with first one side of the mouth and then the other, sometimes clinging on with such tenacity that they are removed only with difficulty.

The venom of these snakes is of a neurotoxic nature and almost purely paralytic in its action. In direct contrast to the venom of the crotalids, that of the coral snakes cause very little tissue damage at the site of the bite, with little or no swelling. The pain is restricted only to that caused by the puncture of the fangs. This absence of severe pain and edema has been responsible for lulling human victims into a sense of false security in cases where the identity of the snake was not recognized.

Coral snakes are frequently far more plentiful in sections of their range than is generally suspected. This is because of their secretive habits. They are essentially a burrowing snake and spend much of their time foraging about under fallen leaves and beneath the bark of decaying trees. Their diet consists largely of small snakes and lizards which they stun quickly with their venom. This venom, drop for drop, is by far the most toxic of that of any snake found in North America.

After envenomation by a coral snake the victim may not display any symptoms for anywhere from one to several hours. When the poison does begin to take effect, however, it may manifest itself in the form of weakness, giddiness, nausea, apprehension, salivation, vomiting, and a sense of glowing heat. Paralysis, usually of a bulbar type, follows in fatal cases, with death coming from respiratory paralysis.

It was long believed that the tourniquet, incision, and suction were useless in the treatment of coral snake bite. Recent investigation has indicated that at least a small portion of the venom may be removed by this method, and many doctors feel it is worth the effort. It is important that the site of the bite be washed prior to incision in order to remove any excess venom that may be on the skin and which may accidentially be introduced into the flesh by the scalpel.

As in the therapy for bites by any of the crotalids, antivenin is of vital importance where the bite of a coral snake is concerned. At this point it is interesting to note the existence of a distinct deficiency in the field of United State medicine. No drug company in this country, or anywhere else for that matter, is producing a specific antivenin for the North American coral snake.

Fortunately, the Instituto Butantan in Sao Paulo, Brazil, manufactures an antivenin which is specifically for the Brazilian coral snake (*Micrurus corallinus*). This serum has been proved to be highly effective in the treatment of the North American coral snakebite. Here arises a problem, however, since the antivenin manufactured in Brazil is not produced under the auspices of the United States health authorities. In order for health departments, hospitals, and zoos to maintain a supply of this vital serum they are forced to deal with an unlicensed firm. Thus, if the lives of coral snake victims are to be saved in the United States, state agencies and others must break federal trade regulations.

Despite all the red tape and legal problems, numerous hospitals and zoos do maintain a supply of the Brazilian-produced coral snake antivenin, and the Florida Health Department in Jacksonville manages to keep enough on hand to supply the needs of the state and even share with other states when the serum is needed. A research project on the subject is under way at the University of Florida, and it is expected that domestic production of coral snake venom will begin in the next year or so.

In 1962 the Florida State Board of Health made a survey of all reported snakebites in the state. In that year there were 277 bites reported. Many of the statistics gleaned from this study are more or less typical of the snakebite picture for any given year, and they apply in general terms to all areas where snakes are found.

The seasonal pattern shows that most snakebites occur during the summer months, with a high of 44 being reported in August and a low of 8 in February. Of course, the fact that *any* bites occurred in the winter months is due to year-round warm weather peculiar to a large part of the state of Florida. In more-northern states cases of snakebite during the winter months are so rare as to be practically nonexistent.

Seventy-three of the 277 bites were from the diamond-back rattler (*Crotalus adamanteus*), 46 were from the

cottonmouth moccasin (*Agkistrodon piscivorus*), 45 were
from the pygmy rattler (*Sistrurus miliarius*), 8 were from the
copperhead (*Agkistrodon contortrix*), and 7 were from coral
snakes (*Micrurus fulvius*). The remaining 98 bites were inflicted by nonvenomous or unidentified snakes.

Young people—those below the age of twenty—accounted
for more than half of the bites, with three times more boys
being bitten than girls.

The study disclosed that the greater number of bites are
on the fingers, with the feet taking second place and the
lower part of the legs coming in third. Snakes encountered
on the open ground are responsible for the greatest number
of bites. To a lesser extent, bites came from snakes in houses
or other buildings, in gardens, and in patches of weeds. Over
half of the total number of bites occur between the hours of
noon and 6:00 P.M.

11

PERSONAL EXPOSURE

Despite the numerous hazards frequently associated with combat aviation, an encounter with poisonous snakes is seldom considered to be one of them. However, the seemingly impossible can always happen, as witness the following story:

Near the end of World War II a Navy fighter group was assigned to a nowhere sort of air base in the wastelands of Texas. The planes were Grumman Hellcats, and the commanding officer was putting the young pilots through all kinds of training maneuvers designed to simulate conditions that would be encountered when the group was transferred to the forward area in the Pacific. The pilots and ground crews slept in tents, and the planes were parked on the side of a stretch of asphalt that served as a landing strip.

After an early breakfast one torrid July morning the pilots assembled in headquarters tent for briefing and were told they would practice low-level strafing on specified targets on a hillside a few miles away.

"It'll be hot out there this morning," the officer in charge concluded, "but not any hotter than it will be out in the

Pacific. I want everybody to stay in line and rejoin the formation after each run on the target."

After the briefing the planes revved up and charged down the runway one after another. When the last was airborne the chunky little fighters went into formation, and the squadron leader gave the order to attack the hillside targets. The radios crackled as observers and commanders talked with the attacking pilots, and the desert air rattled with the staccato bursts of machine-gun fire. Suddenly, one of the Hellcats nearing the target area seemed to go out of control. It did a quick wing-over, went into a vertical climb, and executed a faltering version of an Immelmann.

The radio conversation between the pilot, squadron leader, and other members of the flight was excited and somewhat confused.

"What's wrong, Fifty-nine?" the squadron commander demanded. "Are you trying to play cowboy or something?"

"Fifty-nine to Blue Leader," the voice came back. "Nothing wrong 'cept there's a rattlesnake in this cockpit and he's trying to crawl up in my lap!"

Everyone who heard the message began to offer advice. Some urged the pilot to jump and take his chances in the parachute. Others suggested opening the canopy and trying to dump the snake out by turning the plane upside down. Still another offered that the snake be caught behind the head and thrown out into the air.

"Thanks for the advice," the young pilot replied. "But I'm going to take this critter upstairs and *hibernate* him."

Ramming the throttle ahead he hung the Hellcat on its propeller and climbed to twenty thousand feet. As the cold air of the upper altitude invaded the cockpit the snake gradually became lethargic and then rigid. The pilot had already snapped on his oxygen mask and was breathing easily. He continued to climb higher and higher until the snake was literally frozen stiff. He then gingerly picked it up and placed it in his map case.

"Fifty-nine to Blue Leader." The words over the radio came in clearly from the high-flying plane. "Request permission to return to base with frozen rattler. Will turn specimen over to medical officer for preservation and study."

History does not relate how many enemy planes this pilot accounted for after he completed his training in Texas and went into battle, nor does it show how many medals he collected. One thing is certain, however, and that is that on that July morning he should have been rewarded with some kind of commendation for fast thinking and knowing enough about reptiles and aerodynamics to save himself from serious injury and for returning his plane to the landing strip in good order.

The snake that had caused the excitement proved to be a desert sidewinder (*Crotalus cerastes*). How or why it found its way into the fighter cockpit will always remain a mystery, but snakes make a habit of venturing into unusual hiding places.

Never let a rattlesnake set up housekeeping in a Thermos jug in the middle of winter and expect to get him out at a specific time. This note of admonishment was personally entered in my herpetological records a few years ago.

I had been invited to appear on a television program to make a brief talk on the subject of snakes. The location was Birmingham, Alabama, and the time was February. I had written an article about snakes that was to appear in the March issue of a national magazine, and the production manager at the television station thought it would be timely to have me on one of his shows. He wondered also if it would be possible to have a live snake to spike up the interest. I agreed, and later that day telephoned Ross Allen in Silver Springs, Florida, and explained my problem. He obligingly consented to ship a live rattlesnake to me. When the snake arrived a couple of days later there was a scattering of snow on the ground, and the temperature was hovering a few degrees above zero.

Until the appointed day I kept the snake inside the house in a nice tight cage built for the purpose. When the day for the television show arrived I allowed myself a full hour for travel to the station. Backing the car out of the garage I turned on the heater. I wanted the car to be warm so the snake would be in a lively condition when he made his debut before the camera. As fate would have it, the fan on the heater chose that moment to go on the blink. There was no time to have it repaired so I did the next best thing and called a taxi.

When the driver appeared at the door he asked if there would be any luggage. Quite innocently I told him I had a rattlesnake to go, but that I would carry the cage out to the cab myself.

"Not in *my* hack!" the driver said vehemently, his breath making clouds of vapor in the cold air. "I've hauled a lot of things—drunks, sick dogs and women in labor, but I'll be . . ."

He stomped back down the icy walk that led to the street, and I knew there was no use in trying to reason with him.

The television show was now less than forty-five minutes away, and I had fully ten miles to drive through city traffic. By taking short cuts I could still make it, but I knew the snake would be dead by the time I arrived unless there was some way to keep him warm. It was then that I thought of the gallon Thermos jug on a shelf in the pantry. Its thick insulation would certainly keep a snake at room temperature for the drive across town, even in a cold car.

Lifting the rattler from his cage with my snake stick, I eased him down into the jug and screwed the top on tightly.

When I finally reached the studio the man in charge of the program was obviously irritated because of my last-minute arrival. The stage crew had constructed a large box in the middle of the floor to contain the promised snake, and one of the cameras was mounted on a mobile tripod above the structure.

"We have only about five minutes," the director said. "I'll want your snake in the middle of that box so my camera can get a good tight shot of him as we open the show."

Tossing my topcoat and gloves onto a chair I looked around for my snake stick. Just then I remembered that I had left it at home. Concerned, but not really worried, I removed the top from the Thermos and tried to shake the rattler out into the box. Nothing happened! Turning the jug up I looked inside. The snake was there all right, but he apparently found the security of the jug to his liking and he had no intention of forsaking his new abode. He had formed several coils and each of them was tightly pressed against the inside wall of the jug. The harder I tried to dislodge him, the more obstinate he became.

I had often heard that the scenes that take place behind the curtain in the world of the theater are frequently more interesting than those which the audience sees across the footlights. At that moment I was quite willing to agree.

On the studio wall the big electric clock seemed to glare down at me as the minute hand climbed toward its zenith.

I had never been on a television program before, and none of the people in the studio had ever been called upon to open a show with a live rattlesnake as the guest star. Tempers flared and the floor manager consulted control room technicians through intercom mikes and finally someone with an ominous-sounding voice announced that air time would be in one minute.

"It'll make a funny shot, anyway," I heard some wag mumble. "We'll get a picture of a guy trying to empty a lemonade jug."

"He's probably faking and hasn't got a snake in there anyway," someone else said.

The derisive comments rankled. Here I had gone to the trouble of importing a live rattlesnake, keeping it in my home for several days, and then I had fought like a tiger to get it to the studio on time. I was not going to be outdone. Just then someone began a countdown: "Ten seconds—nine —eight—"

Directed more by anger than common sense, I impulsively thrust my right hand down into the Thermos jug and grabbed the recalcitrant snake by a coil, yanked him out and flipped him into the middle of the box. A red light above the studio door winked on, and above me I saw the massive camera pointing toward my rattler. Chancing a quick glance across the studio at a monitor I saw the picture that the viewers at home were watching. It was perfect. The instant he had been extracted from the jug and tossed into his pen, the rattler had drawn himself into a classic pose—body bunched in tight coils, head upraised, and his string of rattles buzzing like an alarm clock.

The next day a friend stopped me on the street and told me he had watched the show. "That opening shot of the live snake was pretty effective," he opined. "Guess television stations have all kind of film clips like that that they get from Hollywood, don't they?"

I resisted an urge to expound at length and tell the man exactly how he came to experience his vicarious thrill at the sight of an angry rattlesnake performing on his tube. He probably would not have believed my story anyway.

In 1951 R. Marlin Perkins,* who at that time was director of the Lincoln Park Zoo in Chicago, had a more serious affair with a camera-shy snake. At the time Perkins was conducting a network television program called *Zoo Parade*.

About twenty minutes before air time on a Sunday morning he was positioning a timber rattler (*Crotalus horridus*) on a desk so the cameras could get a good opening shot. The snake stick he was using slipped and the rattler struck. One of its fangs entered Perkins' middle finger. He immediately opened the fang puncture with his pocketknife, applied a tourniquet, and began suction. Within ten minutes he was on his way to a hospital while his associate Lear Grimmer took over the show.

The bite proved to be serious, and it was three weeks before Perkins could resume his television program.

Some people have such an abiding fear of snakes that they will go to almost any extent to take evasive action when confronted with one. Two friends of mine once got themselves embroiled in a predicament that could have had tragic results, but happily became little more than a comedy of errors.

The two men, Henry Marshall and Al French, were on a hunting trip in a Georgia swamp, and to reach a ridge of high ground known to abound with squirrels they borrowed a dilapidated bateau from a local trapper. As they were stowing their guns and other equipment aboard the boat the old trapper casually mentioned that they should be cautious when paddling beneath overhanging bushes. The weather

* Currently director of the St. Louis Zoological Park.

was unseasonably warm for fall, and there might be some water moccasins trying to take full advantage of the waning sunlight by resting in the branches, he explained.

Marshall and French paddled along the twisting stream that meandered through the swamp to the ridge, and after several hours of hunting they returned to the boat. It was late afternoon and the swamp was alive with the sounds of scolding jays, rasping crickets, and the raucous chuckle of yellowhammers. Long shadows were leaning across the stream as they dug at the coffee-colored water with their crude paddles. Marshall was in the bow of the bateau, and French was on the stern seat. As they passed under an overhanging limb of a jack oak that was matted solid with a flame vine there was a sudden movement and a thick-bodied water moccasin tumbled out of the foliage and thumped into the bottom of the boat like a length of heavy wet rope.

Henry Marshall spun around on his seat and chopped down at the creature with his paddle. The handle broke and the snake struck at the blade.

"Leave him alone, Henry!" Al French shouted. "Maybe he'll go over the side."

Henry Marshall was terrified at the sight of the moccasin, however, and even if he heard his friend's advice he did not take heed. Instead, he snatched up his 12-gauge double-barreled shotgun and pulled both triggers. The twin blasts shook the swamp, and a flock of roosting crows splattered themselves against the sky, squawking their protest.

If nothing else, Henry Marshall's aim had been good, and what remained of the snake writhed and twisted about in the bottom of the boat, but the nearly four hundred No. 4 shot had cut a ragged hole in the floorboards, and water was pouring in at an alarming rate. Frantically, they looked about for a place to beach the boat, but there was no solid ground in sight. Each side of the slough was covered with a rank growth of reeds and vines.

Marshall stripped off his flannel shirt and tried to plug the leak with it. In his zeal to stop the ingress of water he pushed too hard on his crumpled shirt and all at once it went completely through. With no other caulking available he wriggled out of his pants and crammed them into the hole; losing his billfold in the process.

For the next few minutes the two nimrods exchanged frightened and angry words, but when the verbal storm subsided they had evolved a plan that was to get them safely back to the trapper's cabin where they had borrowed the boat. Al French remained on the stern seat and continued to paddle while his friend sat on the rent in the bottom of the boat to keep the pants in place. There was a rusty coffee can aboard and Marshall used it to bail out the water that seeped in around his buttocks.

It is doubtful if there exists a true herpetologist or seasoned naturalist who has not at one time or another found himself in a situation involving a snake in which he would have to admit that he was just plain scared.

I think my closest experience of such fear came one time when I was on an exploration trip in Central America. Our base was the coastal town of Puerto Cortez, Honduras, and on this particular occasion I had journeyed alone back into the interior on a private expedition. My camping gear consisted only of the contents of a canvas packsack on my back. It had rained almost incessantly each of the three nights I had been on the trail. On the afternoon of the fourth day I came upon a deserted and somewhat dilapidated shack that had possibly been built a few years earlier by mining prospectors. The humble abode was far from posh accommodations, but at least it boasted a tin roof and a makeshift sort of bunk bed built against the rear wall.

In the fading light of the setting sun I cooked supper over a small fire which I built in front of the cabin. Then, when darkness came on, I went inside and stretched out on the bare boards of the bunk. Mosquitoes and other insects did their best to make life miserable, but at least I had found a dry place to sleep. With the protection of a bottle of insect repellent I relaxed and listened to the night sounds of the jungles.

All around there was the chatter and babble of monkeys and night birds and the underlying din of frogs and insects. Then, for the fourth straight night, the rains came. First, there was a windy shower of spray that rattled on the roof. This gradually increased to the drumming sound of a heavy downpour as I dozed off to sleep.

Later that night the noise of a violent thunderstorm moving into the area awakened me. Flashes of lightning illuminated the cabin and my wrist watch showed that the time was 2:00 A.M. I shifted about on my bunk and longed for a more comfortable bed, but after three nights of soggy dampness I was thankful that I had a dry place to sleep. Rolling over on my left side I propped myself on my elbow and watched the approach of the storm through an open window near the door. Wind whipped through the vine-laced jungles and rattled the fronds of nearby palms as the center of the front drew nearer. Flashes of lightning became more brilliant and frequent, and thunder boomed through the darkness and shook the walls of the cabin.

Fascinated by the violent display of the elements, I continued to watch and noticed that during the flashes of lightning I could see everything in the cabin almost as clearly as if the room had been flooded with sunlight. Across from my Spartan bunk was a crude table on which I had placed my haversack, .38 revolver, and two-cell flashlight. It was while I was looking toward the table that I caught sight of something moving on the floor. In the fleeting instant of illumination I saw that it was a snake. I saw, too, the peculiar cross-hatch markings on its body. It was a fer-de-lance and a big one! I sat bolt upright on my bunk and stared into the now inky blackness of the small room.

Barbamaria is the name the natives of Central America have given the fer-de-lance (*Bothrops atrox*). As has been pointed out, more properly it is Barba Amarilla, which translated into English means yellow beard—a name derived from the yellow wash of color on the underside of the lower jaw. The fer-de-lance, along with the tropical rattlesnake, bushmaster, and palm viper, is one of the most dangerously poisonous snakes found in all tropical America. Its venom contains both hemotoxic and neurotoxic properties, and death for its victims is almost certain unless extensive medical attention can be secured immediately. I recalled the death of a banana plantation worker near Puerto Cortez who had been bitten by one of these snakes while clearing away a rubbish heap.

When my friend Earl Handley and I had found him only minutes after he had been bitten, the whites of the man's eyes had become red and there were repeated hemorrhages from his stomach as well as a constant discharge of blood from the mucous walls of his throat and mouth. The *mozo*, or plantation worker, had been struck by a five-foot specimen of a fer-de-lance, and he was dead an hour later. The creature that had entered the cabin with me was fully seven feet in length.

Every vestige of sleep erased from my mind, I sat there on my bunk staring into the darkness and thinking about the apparition that had been momentarily revealed to me. Hopefully, I reasoned the snake had entered the cabin to wait out the storm. Perhaps it would lie beneath the table until the rain had stopped and then glide back out into the jungle to continue its night of hunting.

Lightning flashed again and once more I saw the snake. It was moving away from the table and out toward the middle of the room. In a flashbulb-instant of illumination I saw it pause, lance-shaped head uplifted and forked tongue sampling the air for smells.

Perhaps, I thought, this cabin was a spot the fer-de-lance made as part of its regular rounds. I had guessed the place had been deserted for years, and maybe the reptile had found by experience that this shelter would occasionally provide a meal in the form of a jungle rat or small monkey that might chance to hole up there from time to time.

I knew the snake would object to my intrusion as much as I resented its. I knew, too, that it would expect me to keep out of its way the same as it would expect any other creature such as a tapir or peccary to sense its presence and retreat before its advance. Lightning, that had moments before been flashing almost constantly, perversely came to a virtual stand-still. The agonizing darkness persisted, and I felt myself growing more tense with each passing second. I cursed my stupidity for leaving my flashlight and gun on the table at the opposite side of the room. For a moment I toyed with the idea of jumping off my bunk and running across the room toward the table. The odds were in my favor that I could make it, but there was also the chance that I might step squarely on the snake.

A ragged bolt of lightning clawed down from a cloud and shattered a ceiba tree near the cabin, filling the air with the smell of ozone. The resulting clap of thunder was deafening. The near miss of lightning would, itself, have been unnerving, but in the harsh white light that flooded the cabin I had seen the snake again. It seemed to be flowing like a stream of living liquid across the rough boards of the floor—not going anywhere in particular, but just slowly exploring. Inky darkness again and the rumble of thunder and the drumming of the rain. I was sitting on my bunk and my breath was coming in short gasps. I felt streams of perspiration sliding down my face, and I knew it was not from the heat because the storm had cooled the night air.

Again there was a long interval of darkness followed by a weak and flickering flash of lightning. This time the snake was nowhere to be seen. I wondered if maybe he had departed. Lightning again and this time I happened to be looking in the right direction. The fer-de-lance was sliding up onto the foot of my bunk!

I jumped and hit the middle of the cabin floor with such force that my knees buckled, and I went down in a splinter-gathering slide that carried me directly beneath the table. The impact knocked it upside down, spilling my packsack, canteen, flashlight, and other items on the floor. I clawed at the jumble around me, and my fingers closed around the cold metal of the flashlight. Fumbling with the switch I snapped it on and swung the beam about the cabin.

The snake had drawn itself up onto the bunk, but now it was pouring its length back down to the floor. Its head was held high and its tongue was flicking in and out at a rapid rate. I pawed at the gunbelt and yanked the revolver from the holster. The first shot hit the middle of the body and writhing coils twisted and convulsed as if a tangled rope was being violently shaken. I shot again and again at the frightful mass until the hammer clicked on an empty shell.

Tucking the flashlight under my left armpit I picked up the gunbelt and got to my feet. As I slipped six fresh cartridges into the cylinder I watch the dying snake's convulsions gradually subside.

All thoughts of sleep had been swept away. I put the table

back on its legs and climbed up on top of it and sat there until dawn began to filter through the rain-drenched jungles. When it was light enough to see I got down and stretched the kinks from my tired muscles.

When I measured the dead snake I found it was almost exactly seven feet in length, and three of my hastily fired bullets had hit the mark. One of them had severed the spine, another had ripped a hole in the belly, and the third had cut a gash in the neck. It is, of course, possible that two of the wounds may have been made by the same bullet, but how the wounds were inflicted were of little importance. All I was concerned with was that the snake was dead.

Reflecting on the nightmarish episode, I am convinced that I would react in exactly the same manner now as I did then if confronted with the same problem. I know now, as I knew at the time, that the foraging fer-de-lance had not entered the cabin to do me harm. I still believe it simply came in to get out of the rain, but once inside it and I became enemies. If I had not awakened when I did, and it had come up on the bunk with me, it would likely have turned away as soon as it found me. Had I made any kind of movement, however, it is almost certain that it would have interpreted it as an act of aggression, and it would almost certainly have countered with a strike.

12

LORE

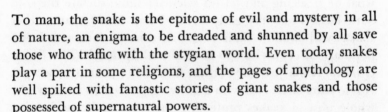

To man, the snake is the epitome of evil and mystery in all of nature, an enigma to be dreaded and shunned by all save those who traffic with the stygian world. Even today snakes play a part in some religions, and the pages of mythology are well spiked with fantastic stories of giant snakes and those possessed of supernatural powers.

With all his erudition, modern man is still awed at the sight of a garter snake that has invaded the flower garden beside his house. People who have devoted their lives to such complex studies as electronics, space exploration, chemistry, and the construction of giant buildings are often just as gullible about snake tales as the most illiterate backwoodsman. It is widely believed, for instance, that some snakes have a fang or stinger on the tip of their tails like a scorpion. Others can break apart and later reassemble their bodies, and there is a *deadly poisonous* snake in North America known as the spreading adder. Lore accords some snakes the power to charm or hypnotize birds and other creatures they wish to catch. Then, of course, who has not heard of how mother snakes swallow their young in time of danger?

Should they be asked if any of these or the many other beliefs are true, most people will hedge and finally admit that they are not quite sure.

Those of us who have been fortunate enough to be able to divide our research between the fastness of the tall timbers and the book-lined walls of the study are less prone to scoff at folklore than is the academician who is restricted to the laboratory and the review of accepted papers. Both play an important part in the study of nature, but the field naturalist has a better opportunity to come face-to-face with some of the unexplainable quirks of nature.

Most snake tales are just pure fiction, but there are times when the conscientious naturalist is hard pressed to ignore what he is seeing and let his scientific mind dictate the cold hard facts. From my early youth I had heard that mother snakes will swallow their young in time of danger, a belief popularized centuries ago in Edmund Spenser's *The Faerie Queene*. It was just one of those facts that a youngster accepts. A few years later, and with a growing interest in zoology, the whole idea of snakes protecting their young by swallowing them was ridiculous. Ridiculous, that is, until one summer afternoon when I happened to be strolling along the bank of a stream in central Alabama and was suddenly confronted with the sight of a large water moccasin *swallowing her young!*

The snake on the sandy bank ahead of me was fully three feet in length and near the midsection it was nearly five inches in diameter. As I eased closer I saw a dozen or so of the baby snakes that had not had time to be swallowed skittering away in all directions. I killed the "mother" snake, and then to satisfy my curiosity I split her open from the neck down to the middle of the abdominal region and removed the stomach and gullet. There were two snakes inside. The one in the gullet was still alive but a bit groggy. I tied him up in my handkerchief to keep for further study. The little one inside the stomach was dead, but it looked just like the other. When I returned home I made a careful study of my little serpentine Jonah, and there was no question but that it was a newly hatched racer (*Coluber constrictor constrictor*). The "mother" moccasin had simply happened along at the time the little racers were hatching and was simply feeding on them.

Had I not been suspicious of the color and shape of the little snakes I might have been content to believe that the books and logic were all wrong. Anyway, it is a good case in point to demonstrate how even a conscientious observer of nature can be duped into believing a tale that has found its way into the folklore of snakes. Then, just to add to the confusion and substantiate the belief, many snakes are viviparous. If a gravid female is killed and cut open shortly before she is ready to give birth, the little snakes will begin to crawl away. If, in a hypothetical case, a man should happen upon a pregnant water moccasin or any other water snake eating young snakes of another species and then cut her open and find her full of live young ones, it would be difficult to persuade him to believe that mother snakes do not swallow their young in time of danger. But it is not so, since the only route from a snake's mouth is straight down the gullet and into the stomach. Once there, powerful digestive juices would quickly dissolve any kind of flesh and bone.

American folklore's spreading adder is a serpent to be killed on sight, or better still to be avoided if at all possible. Many believe this snake to be a North American counterpart of the cobras of Asia and Africa. In various parts of the country it is also known by such ominous-sounding names as the puff adder, hissing viper, blow snake, and spread head. It is credited with being able to injure seriously and even kill man and beast by simply blowing its poisonous breath in their face.

This contemporary basilisk is none other than the common hognose snake (*Heterodon* spp). In one form or another it is found throughout most of the country from New England west to Montana, south to the Mexican border, and east to Florida.

Of all snakes in North America, the hognose, or hognosed as it is sometimes called, is my top choice for a pet. It is docile, easy to feed, and no more harmful than a canary. If this is so it is logical then to wonder why it has such a bad reputation. The answer lies in the buffoonery it demonstrates when first encountered.

Suppose you are strolling through a sunlit wood on a summer morning and chance to rest beside a tall pine. Seating yourself on a granite boulder you suddenly hear a sharp hissing sound nearby, like air escaping from an aerosol bomb. When you turn you see a two-foot snake, with a thick body menacingly coiled. The head is upraised and the neck is flattened like a cobra. As you jump to your feet the snake strikes and misses your leg by a fraction of an inch. If you do not know the hognose snake you will probably scramble around and find a stick large enough to club the life out of the serpent. If you are superstitious and have heard of this "deadly" snake, you may run away clutching your throat and struggling for a fresh breath of air to clear your lungs of the venomous fumes blown at you by the hissing viper.

But if you tarry and goad the snake into further aggression, you will witness one of nature's little comedians going through its act. To make the sound that first attracted your attention, the hognose snake inflated its lung with air and blew it forcefully through its nostrils. Adding impetus to the menacing sound it flattened its neck and lashed out in a strike that would do credit to a diamondback rattler. What is more it will strike again and again, but always manage narrowly to miss its target.

When all of the sound and fury fails to put the intruder to flight, this funny little clown of the serpent world will suddenly pretend that it has been seriously injured. To prove its point, it will begin to writhe about on the ground with its mouth hanging open in a pitiful manner. As it scrubs its head from one side to the other bits of dirt and debris cling to the slack jaws, making it appear that the head has been crushed. After its death scene has been played for a minute or so the hognose finally "expires" and rolls over on its back and lies completely motionless. At this point it may be picked up and tossed about and for all practical purposes it is really dead—or so it seems. If it is replaced on the ground in the upside down position it assumed, it will remain motionless. If, however, it is returned to the ground so that it is lying on its belly, it will *insist* that it is dead by instantly flipping over on its back again.

The strange antics of the hognose snake are just another of the baffling phases of nature. Upon witnessing such a performance one is prone to wonder why a creature with a supposedly dullish brain has developed such a two-act play. Many snakes hiss, but no nonpoisonous ones quite so menacingly as the hognose. Too, how and why did it develop the cobralike trick of spreading its neck? Most snakes will strike and actually bite if sufficiently aroused, and they often injure their mouth in so doing. The hognose snake seems to know this and resorts to its feinting type of strike, which is often as effective in producing fright as a real strike that could damage its mouth.

Once the hognose has been captured it grows tame, allowing itself to be handled with no repeat of his comical performance. It makes a good companion for people who are inclined to keep snakes as pets. Feeding is simple, as adults feed almost exclusively on toads.

Another of the most preposterous tales in all of snakedom has the hoop snake being capable of grasping its tail in its mouth and going rolling off through the woods like a runaway bicycle tire. Of course, this is impossible, but there are many honest people who will stoutly claim they have actually witnessed this phenomenon.

Once while strolling through the Chickahominy swamps in Virginia I saw two men who were absolutely convinced that they had just seen a hoop snake rolling away from them. I had been standing near the bank of the river when I heard a great commotion in a stand of willows. Turning, I saw two timber cutters plunging along with their axes held over their heads like Indians on the warpath. For a startled moment I stood there wondering if they were coming after me for some reason. Then one of them saw me and shouted in an excited voice, asking if I had seen the hoop snake.

"It was a real hoop snake, all right," the second man panted as the two stopped running and leaned against trees to catch their breath. "Me and my buddy, here, parked up on the road, and we was aiming to pick some blackberries to take home with us when we seen this great big hoop snake lying there in the woods."

"He was shore a big 'ern," the other man agreed. He dropped his ax and extended his arms out to each side, looking reflectively at first one palm and then the other. "Must'er been that wide across. When he seen us he started rolling off down the hill straight toward the river. He was coming this way and it's a wonder he didn't run smack over you."

Deciding to give up the chase, the two men repeated the story of how they had come upon a large dark snake lying in a circle with its tail grasped in its mouth and how it had flipped up and rolled away at their approach.

"Me and my daddy seen one when I was little," one of the timber cutters related. "You know they got a stinger on the tail 'stead of in the mouth like other snakes. He got so mad he stuck it in a pine tree, and 'fore that week was out that old pine was dead as a nit!"

One who enjoys hearing interesting stories soon learns that it is unwise to argue with the teller, so I listened and learned a lot about hoop snakes and some other snakes I had never heard of before.

It is important to remember that most superstitions have at least a seed of truth in them. It is known that certain snakes such as the mud snake and the rainbow snake frequently rest in a circular position with the head near the tail. I have also seen black racers lie in a similar manner. When the two men chanced upon whatever type of snake they had seen it was probably lying in a position that made it look like a hoop. That was as far as the truth went. From there on imagination took over. The snake undoubtedly awakened and reacted swiftly, thrusting its body into action and vanishing into the undergrowth.

The two men were already conditioned to believe in the existence of hoop snakes, and they saw what they wanted to see. Perhaps just at the moment of their approach a rabbit or a pig or some other animal they did not see went scurrying away through the dense undergrowth and the noise convinced them that it was the sound of the fast-rolling snake.

Then there is the question of the "stinger" on the tail that contains a poison so potent that it can kill a tree. Again, there is a seed of truth, for the mud snake (*Farancia abacura*) does have something that might be termed a "stinger" on the tip of his tail. Actually it is a horny spine and often sharp. If one of these snakes is picked up it will wrap its tail around an arm and press the spine down against the flesh. Since they grow to a length of four feet and are very muscular, the digging of the spine can hurt, but it is in no manner poisonous.

Even more ridiculous is the belief that snakes can sting with their tongues. This has probably stemmed from the fact that this fragile sense organ bears a slight resemblance to the stingers at the tip of the abdomen on such insects as bees and wasps. Touching a snake's tongue is about like touching a small rubber band and just as harmless.

Another preposterous belief concerns the milk snake, a member of the king snake (*Lampropeltis*) clan. Many people are certain that this snake attaches itself to the teats of cows and draws milk from the udder while poor old Bossy contentedly chews her cud.

Anyone who has ever milked a cow knows it is quite particular about the manner in which its mammary glands are handled. Should a snake with a bony mouth filled with sharp teeth suddenly take hold, any but the most phlegmatic cow would likely stampede the herd with her reaction. The hungry snake would hardly have time to take the first sip before it was shaken loose and probably trampled into the earth.

Farmers whose daily chore is to milk their cows are the propagators of the milk snake story, although they are the ones who should know the most about kine and be the first to scoff at the idea. It originated, no doubt, with the illiterate farmer who pondered the reason for his cows becoming less productive. Finding no answer readily available, he elected to pin the blame on man's age-old enemy the serpent. So effective has been the condemnation that at least five of the North American king snakes have been permanently labeled with such specific names as the red milk snake, the western milk snake, Cope's milk snake, and others. The milk-stealing belief is not restricted entirely to the farmer and his bovine. Certain tribes in Central America and South America are confident milk snakes invade human domiciles at night and sup from the breasts of lactating women while they sleep.

To draw milk from the teat of cow or woman, a calf or human infant must purse the mouth and fold the tongue around the nipple. A snake would be powerless to perform such an act, since the anatomy of its mouth is entirely different from mammals. Nevertheless, the belief still continues, and annually farmers kill countless numbers of milk snakes when they invade their barns in search only of mice and rats that destroy millions of dollars worth of grain and other feed each year.

One of the strongest beliefs about the unusual powers of snakes is their supposed ability to "charm" birds, people, and animals. No snake has the magic power to hypnotize or charm another creature unless the subject has some unreasoning fear of snakes in general that can induce a sort of temporary paralysis. I recall one cruel prank that I saw some youngsters play on another one of their group one summer afternoon when they were hiking through the countryside in Virginia.

Several of the boys spotted a medium-size black snake and killed it with rocks. While the creature was still writhing with reflex action they picked it up and threw it down in front of a fourteen-year-old boy who was known to be deathly afraid of snakes. As the terrified youngster stared down at the twisting and convulsing coils of the dying snake his face drained of color and when a long moment had passed he fainted.

Fortunately for all concerned, the boy was quickly revived, but had the youngster had a weak heart the episode might have ended with tragic results.

Another time I was riding along a trail in north Alabama, and as I approached a cluster of cabins that were the homes of sawmill workers, I heard a woman screaming. Reining my horse, I stepped down from the saddle and hurriedly made my way through a thicket of underbrush toward the sound of the voice. I found a middle-age woman standing at rigid attention at the edge of a cornfield. Her arms were stiff at her sides, and her wide open eyes were staring at a coiled timber rattler about five feet in front of her. The terrified woman's high-pitched screams were so loud that the sound of the rattler's buzzing tail was drowned out. Placing my hand on her shoulder I attempted to push her away, but she would not be moved. She was in no immediate danger, since the snake was not more than three feet in length and could not have reached her had it decided to strike.

Picking up a large stick I killed the snake with several blows. Almost as if by magic the spell was broken, and the terror-stricken woman ceased her screaming and sank to the ground trembling and sobbing.

While I was pushing the snake farther away with the stick I saw several men and women running from the cabins. When they reached us I told them the woman had been badly frightened by the rattler, but that I did not believe she had been bitten.

"She ain't been bit," one of the women said after a cursory examination. "But her sister died right out here in this same corn patch not more'n a year ago when a snake charmed her and then bit her."

Birds are frequently supposed to be hypnotized by snakes and almost everyone who has spent considerable time in the outdoors observing nature has his own personal tale to tell on the subject. The late Raymond L. Ditmars, who was for so long the Curator of Mammals and Reptiles at the New York Zoological Park, gave a concise and accurate description of what so many of us have witnessed when he wrote on the subject in his book *Snakes of the World*.*

The blacksnake is alleged to resort to the "power" of charming its prey. Allegation of this habit has been applied to various kinds of snakes. As the assertion largely relates to the charming of birds it is not difficult to reach an explanation of its origin.

Many birds have a habit of luring enemies from their nests. They may drag their way along the ground, trailing a wing as if it were broken, but ready to quickly dart forward, or fly, if the interested enemy seeks to grasp them.

A snake in a tree, possibly wandering without definite intent, approaches a nest containing young birds. The mother bird is terrified and seeks to turn the enemy from her brood. Hopping from branch to branch toward the snake she flutters her wings to attract its attention. The snake may not be hungry—and again it may see the nest with the tempting food. The parent bird is desperate. She comes closer to the snake. Her wings droop and she appears to sag. The snake considers one thing even though it may not be particularly hungry. If a meal is easily obtainable as this it is well to take advantage of it. It starts for the bird, anticipating an immediate catch.

The anticipated prey painfully retreats a few inches. The snake follows. The retreat continues, but the reptile's appetite has become stimulated. Its mind has now become set upon the capture of that bird, which lures the reptile to the end of a branch and over another interlacing with an adjacent tree. With the serpent well out of the way the bird flys off, the job well done.

Having noted this going on and in some instances being attracted to it by other birds watching the performance and scolding vigorously from near-by trees I have thought how an observer might form the surmise that the bird so

* New York: The Macmillan Company, 1931, pages 68–69.

strangely fluttering near the snake was "charmed" and attracted toward the reptile.

Occasional birds get into trouble during this luring process. They fail to accurately account for a lateral, striking S the snake may be craftily forming of its anterior part. There is no doubt about the bird taking note of this, but that loop is deceiving. Carried as a well-opened S it looks particularly menacing and is readily gauged, but the snake has a method of greatly enlarging the loop by drawing it together and at the same time feeding its body into the rearward portion. Any closer approach of the bird may bring it into the striking zone. It is a case of being checkmated at its own game.

Surveys show that children account for the largest percentage of snakebite victims in North America. Of this group the very young, in the age bracket between two and five years, are often involved, and it occasionally seems that the child was actually hypnotized.

I recall a particularly harrowing experience in which I was personally involved a few years ago on a California ranch. My host was having a barbecue and there were about a dozen adults gathered on the patio waiting for the charcoal fire to come to just the right temperature before the T-bone steaks were placed on the grill. It was late afternoon, and the setting sun was casting long shadows over the patio and garden. Gradually we became aware of the excited barking of a dog.

"Better go see what Flip has found this time, or he'll never shut up," my host said, getting up from his lawn chair. "He barks at everything that isn't nailed to the floor."

Several of us left the patio and strolled across the garden toward the sound of the barking dog. As we rounded an ornamental palm we were confronted with a terrifying sight. My host's two-year-old son was seated on the ground babbling contentedly while directly in front of him and not more than four feet away was a coiled rattlesnake.

The child was naturally unaware of his peril and as my friend gasped and started to rush forward I grabbed his shoulder and restrained him. At the moment the rattler was preoccupied with the antics of the excited dog. Undoubtedly it recognized the animal as a more serious threat than the baby. I was afraid that if the father rushed toward his child, the snake's attention might be suddenly diverted, and in the excitement it might strike the baby.

The father began to tremble and his breath came in labored gasps. I ordered him to stand where he was and dropped to my hands and knees, crawling up behind the child like an animal sneaking up on its prey. I knew I was in no danger, so it was not an act of courage on my part. My only problem was to keep the desperate father from exciting the snake while I slipped up behind the child. In a frightening moment the thought crossed my mind that the baby might suddenly turn his head and see me. If he attempted to flounce away the snake would strike him for sure. When I was within arm's reach I grabbed the little fellow by his left ankle and snatched him toward me.

Startled, and I am sure hurt by the sudden rough handling, he screamed. The father could contain himself no longer and rushed in to grab up his child, certain that the outcry had been caused by the fangs of the snake.

In the ensuing minutes one event followed swiftly on the heels of another. The baby was rushed back to the safety of the house and someone produced a shotgun. When the charge of shot had dispatched the snake and all of us had time to settle down after bestowing praise upon the alert little dog, I took a tape back down to the spot and measured the dead snake. It was a western diamondback and measured three feet, nine inches in length.

After the narrow escape the party spirit was gone for the afternoon, and I seem to remember that the spunky little dog was generously rewarded with all of the T-bones he wanted.

Although health department records disclose that some very young children are seriously or fatally injured by snakes, there is also evidence that an unusual relationship sometimes seems to exist between human infants and such creatures as the rattlesnake.

One Texas mother walked out in the backyard one day and promptly fainted when she discovered her three-year-old daughter casually petting a large rattlesnake as if it had been the family cat. When the woman revived by natural means she found her child had forsaken the snake without harm and by then was contentedly digging a hole in the sandy yard with a discarded tablespoon.

On another occasion the principal of an elementary school in a small Florida town was greatly shocked when one of his pupils walked into his office with a three-foot live coral snake draped around her neck. The little girl's *boy friend* had given it to her at recess, and she wanted to know if the principal would keep it for her until it was time to go home.

Incidents where children have come through such perilous encounters unscathed are numerous, but because the human infant and even the young child have no fear of snakes, many have been injured and killed. It seems this fear is one that humans must acquire as they grow older, in direct contrast with other creatures such as birds, monkeys, dogs, and cats, which all appear to come into the world with an abiding dread of snakes.

There is a strong belief that a camper has only to surround his bed with a length of rope and he will be safe from attack by poisonous snakes during the night. The legend probably began a century or so ago when cowboys and prospectors bedded down on the desert sands in their blankets. Perhaps half a dozen times during the day they had seen deadly snakes and desperately longed for something that would protect them during the night.

Herpetologists have made careful investigation to determine if a snake will refuse to cross a rope, and there is laboratory proof that this, as with so many other snake stories, is just fiction. However, it is unwise to scoff at *any* belief that has stood the test of time for over a hundred years. As a matter of fact, there is considerable evidence to prove that a well-worn lariat, permeated with man's smell, encircling the bedroll will deter the invasion by a meandering sidewinder or gila monster.

Under laboratory testing a caged snake will crawl over a piece of rope as quickly as he would over a pebble or a board. This is because he is a captive and is constantly seeking a route to escape, just as a Bengal tiger stalks his cage.

Man and his lore have given the joint snake an entirely different trick of magic. As the tale is told, should you strike this snake with a stick it will shatter as if it were made of glass, but after you have gone away the various pieces will reassemble and the joint snake will glide away none the worse for the experience.

Here again there is just a hint of truth tucked away in this legend. The joint snake, or glass snake as it is alternately called, is almost as interesting in reality as it is in folklore.

To the casual observer, the joint snake is to all intent and purpose a snake in the truest sense of the word. A typical example in North America is *Ophisaurus ventralis,* which may grow to a length of over two feet. He has a snakelike body covered with closely compressed glistening scales. When resting he often coils like a snake, and when he moves he slithers through the grass in true snake fashion. But the glass or joint snake is not a snake at all. It is instead a legless lizard, perhaps a modern-day representative of the first snakes which decided they could propel their elongated bodies through the grass and underbrush more swiftly without legs. The legless lizard is as smooth from head to tail as any snake on earth, and it could pass for a true snake at any Sunday School picnic.

The legend about it no doubt stems from the ability of some lizards, including the so-called joint snake, to drop or shed their tails upon being caught. The tail is in no way connected to the spinal column but is filled with muscles that will cause it to flip about with reflex action in the grass for a minute or so after it is severed from the body. This section of the tail flouncing about in the grass acts as a decoy to attract the enemy's attention while the lizard makes good its escape. It is not true that the two parts will rejoin when the danger is past, but the disjointing act causes the lizard no serious damage and in time a new tail will be grown.

It hardly seems possible that one individual snake could be responsible for the deaths of a grandfather, father, and son, each separated by a score of years. But such a story has been told by many people who declare it to be true.

Apparently the first victim, a middle-aged man, was walking through the woods of Georgia inspecting his turpentine trees. Suddenly, he heard a buzzing sound nearby, but before he could get out of the way he was struck by a large diamondback rattlesnake. The fangs entered just above the heel of the left boot. The man hurried to his horse and rode back to his plantation house where he died a few hours later.

Twenty years went by, according to the story, while his infant son grew to manhood, married, sired a son of his own, and took over the management of the family business. One day he chanced upon his father's boots in a trunk and decided to try them on. While he was walking about the grounds he felt a sharp pain in his left foot. A doctor was summoned a short while later when he began to experience strange sensations over his body. From the symptoms, the doctor diagnosed it as a snakebite, although the man was positive he had not been bitten by a snake. Nevertheless, he died.

Time passed and the third generation scion of the turpentine plantation was approaching manhood when, like his father, he discovered the lethal boots. He, too, tried them on for size and died of "snakebite" shortly thereafter.

After the third death was recorded an investigation of the boots was made, and it was discovered that one of the rattlesnake fangs that had bitten the grandfather forty years earlier was still imbedded in the leather of the left boot just above the counter.

It is true that dried snake venom will prove to be just as virulent when reconstituted years later as when first injected from the fang in liquid form. The small amount of crystals that might cling to a single fang, however, would be only mildly toxic to even the most exquisitely sensitive person.

There is something about human nature that causes most people to fear any snake. At the same time they are lured by a sort of morbid fascination for a look at a snake providing they can do so from a safe vantage point. Operators of carnival side shows and showmen in general, recognizing this trait, have exploited it down through the ages.

Any circus or carnival is almost certain to sport at least one concession along the midway that offers the public an opportunity to see live snakes. Often the conditions are so bizarre as to be ridiculous, but as a rule they pack in the customers, and that, after all, is the objective of the show.

One I recall was billed as the Wild Man of Borneo, and the barker outside the tent drew attention to his pitch by tapping his cane on a box containing live rattlesnakes, loudly proclaiming these to be but a few of the wild man's deadly playmates. Once inside the tent there was a long waiting period in semidarkness while the pitchman sought to sell enough tickets to fill the remaining empty seats.

The show finally began with many gutteral snarls and growls coming from behind a curtain followed by a loud hissing sound. At this cue the curtain was parted revealing the wild man "caged" in a canvas pit with iron bars over the top. In true wild man fashion the star stumbled around the bottom of the pit clawing at his mop of scraggly hair and beating on his chest as he glowered menacingly up at the spectators.

To keep him company in his captivity the owners of the show had supplied him with a dozen or so bull, corn, and milk snakes. All were either drugged or so weary with life that they allowed themselves to be picked up and handled with little more than a passive twisting of their coils. During the performance the barker, who had left his platform on the midway and moved into the darkened tent, explained in great detail how all of the snakes had been captured in the steaming jungles, and according to his spiel, each was just a little more deadly than the other. The wild man, he explained, had been bitten so many times that the venom no longer affected him. The climax of the exhibition came when a live chicken was dropped into the pit. With savage snarls the man captured the fowl and bit into its neck, bringing forth a spurt of blood and frantic flapping of wings. At this moment the curtain was drawn and the pitchman explained that the show was over; the wild man must be left in peace to devour his chicken and share parts of it with his pet snakes.

Since there was a show every half hour from five in the afternoon until ten o'clock this would mean the wild man and his snakes daily consumed at least ten chickens. But in the same carnival there was an outdoor restaurant that featured southern fried chicken which I passed up in favor of a bottle of pop and a bag of peanuts.

Another form of snake handling which seems to hold considerable attraction for the public is when a woman and serpent are paired. One I witnessed was billed "Eve and Her Deadly Black Mamba." As would befit the setting, "Eve" was a charming young woman scantily clad in a simulated fig-leaf costume. Her "Deadly Black Mamba," though, was a healthy and amiable specimen of indigo snake about seven feet in length. She did her somewhat sensual dance to the melodic tones of a clarinet and the rhythm of a bongo drummer. As she twisted and turned the snake was allowed to glide around her neck and over her body in a manner that evoked shudders and squeals from the audience.

The traveling medicine man has completely faded from the American scene in the past few decades but around the turn of the century the sight of a covered wagon, its canopy gaily painted with signs, was the assurance of a good show, and the entire population of small towns turned out in mass to listen to a silver-tongued orator extol the virtues of his own special bottled elixir and other health-giving medicaments in his stock. Often as not the itinerate medical drummer would offer a bottle of snakebite remedy, and frequently to assure the skeptics in the audience he would extract a live "deadly" snake from a box and provoke it into biting him. He would then take a swig from his magic bottle, and when he was in good health a quarter of an hour later he found it easy to sell several dozen bottles of his remedy. The snake, of course, was simply a harmless exotic species unfamiliar to the local residents.

Snakebite remedies have at one time or another been sold the world over. In early America the potion generally consisted of a base of grain alcohol with a few evil-tasting herbs and spices mixed in to discourage the family tippler from taking an occasional dose although he had not come in close contact with a snake of any type.

Down through the ages mankind has watched with fascination as members of the human race dared to play with or otherwise expose their anatomy to the fangs of deadly serpents. Even the Christian religion has been rife with the subject of serpents, and there are various cults who cause considerable concern to health departments and other official departments. I once wrote an article for a national magazine and the lead photograph showed me capturing a large rattlesnake. Shortly thereafter I received an impassioned plea from a religious sect in Tennessee noted for their affinity with deadly serpents imploring me to visit the congregation and demonstrate my skill and "obvious faith." I declined as graciously as possible, but I still do not want to spend a holiday in that section of the Volunteer State for fear I might be called upon again.

India has long been characterized by the snake charmer, a turbaned man who squats before an earthen pot or wicker basket and plays wailing notes on a primitive pipe while a deadly hooded cobra sways rhythmically before him. Just why anyone would want to see snake and man addressing one another in such a manner is not readily understandable, but I suspect it goes back to the earlier observation that the serpent invokes an unexplained fascination in man.

The snake charmers of India are members of a cult in which son follows in the steps of father and secrets are handed down from generation to generation. They ply their trade from the tiniest villages along the headwaters of the Ganges to bustling cities from New Delhi to Bombay.

Wherever they perform they never fail to attract an audience, be it barefoot natives or camera-toting tourists.

Snake charming in India is an art and does not involve the use of magic. The men, and sometimes women, learn a great deal about snakes, especially cobras. They are, in fact, herpetologists. They catch their own snakes but, in accordance with their religious belief, keep the creatures captive for only a short period and then return them unharmed to the jungles from which they were taken.

Much as circus performers who work with dogs, snake charmers have learned that not all cobras are good actors. The valuable ones are adroitly removed from the collection and then carefully studied to exploit their most interesting traits.

In the natural state a cobra is quick to take a defensive stand against anything it considers to be a threat to its safety. Its typical behavior pattern is to rear the anterior portion of its body and spread its hood while it strikes and hisses in a menacing manner. Some will do this time after time, while others will yield after a few tries and slither away. It is the persistent ones that are reserved for future shows.

Some snake charmers employ extirpation or surgical removal of the active and reserve fangs of their cobras and others resort to sewing the snake's jaws together. By and large, however, the true artists trust their ability and handle only the unaltered snakes.

For his performance the snake charmer arranges his collection of reptile containers in front of him and then removes the lid from one of the baskets or jars. At that moment he begins his concert on his reed pipe. Because snakes are deaf, the cobra does not hear the sound, but it does see the weaving instrument over its basket and it instantly becomes alert and lifts its head. As it views the unfamiliar surroundings it is usually content to remain in its basket, which it perhaps believes offers some measure of shelter.

The weaving pipe and the swaying body of the man, however, represent danger, and the cobra spreads its hood and begins to twist from one side to the other, searching for an opening to strike. The snake charmer skillfully times the motion of the snake with the wailing notes from his pipe, and to the observer it appears that the snake has truly been charmed and is actually dancing and keeping time to the music. To stop the performance the snake charmer simply withdraws slowly, and the cobra, believing the danger to be past, gradually settles back down into its container, which to it offers a safe hiding place.

If he knows his snakes and is skilled in his trade, two prerequisites to remain long in business, the snake charmer is not really in grave danger. The strike of the cobra is relatively slow in comparison with the lightning-fast jab of the pit vipers. Because of his fixed teethlike fangs the cobra must select a target that will enable him to lock his jaws around an arm or a leg and "chew" his venom into his victim. Knowing this, the snake charmer never allows any part of his body to present such a target.

Thirty to forty thousand people die each year as a direct result of being bitten by poisonous snakes. The vast majority of these deaths occur in India, Asia, South and Central America. The incidence of dangerous snakebite in the United States is relatively low, but each case is potentially a serious one. So serious, in fact, that if not properly treated the victim may die.

Hospital records in the United States record two to three thousand snakebites annually. Most are from nonpoisonous snakes and are potentially no more serious than a scratch from a rose thorn or the claws of a playful kitten. Of this number, however, nearly fifty people in the United States die each year from the bite of poisonous snakes, and five times that number are maimed or permanently disabled. Each year, also, a certain number die from the bites of completely harmless snakes. Some of these victims, as with a percentage of those struck by poisonous snakes, actually die from shock or unreasoning fear. Some have been known to drop dead at the sight of a snake gliding across the grass in front of them.

The record of mortalities from snakebite is not always accurate. For example, should a man die of heart failure after being bitten by a nonpoisonous snake, the attending physician certainly would not list snakebite as the cause of death anymore than he would consider saying a person with a cardiac record died of a heart attack if he were killed in the crash of an airliner. By the same token, a victim of a poisonous snakebite can survive the immediate complications but develop a fatal kidney or liver disorder as a direct result of the injected poison. When several years later he is hospitalized and dies of kidney trouble, the records would not show that this man died of snakebite.

For those who live in the rural and jungle areas of Asia, death by snakebite is still a common occurrence. In the United States, however, such tragedy is comparable to the threat of being struck by lightning.

BIBLIOGRAPHY

Allen, Ross, and Neill, Wilfred T., *Keep Them Alive!* Ross Allen's Reptile Institute, Inc., Silver Springs, Fla., 1959.

"Antivenin (Crotalidae) Polyvalent (equine origin) (North and South American Antisnakebite Serum)." Wyeth Laboratories, Marietta, Pa., 1963.

Criley, B. R., "Development of a Multivalent Antivenin for the Family Crotalidae." *Venoms,* American Assosciation for the Advancement of Science. Reprint from Wyeth Laboratories, Marietta, Pa.

Crompton, John, *Snake Lore.* New York, Doubleday and Company, Inc., 1964.

Dees, John E., M.D., "Florida Snake Bite Date-1963." *The Journal of the Florida Medical Association,* Vol. XLIX, No. 12 (June, 1963), p. 981.

Ditmars, Raymond L. Litt.D., *Reptiles of the World.* New York, MacMillan Company, 1946.

———, *Snakes of the World.* New York, MacMillan Company 1943.

Finley, John C., M.D., "Nature and Treatment of Bites of Venomous Snakes in Canada: A Review." *Canada Medical Association Journal,* (June 27, 1964).

Gingrich, W. C., and Hohenadel, J. C., "Standardization of Polyvalent Antivenin." *Venoms,* American Association for the Advancement of Science. Reprint from Wyeth Laboratories, Marietta, Pa.

Halstead, Bruce W., M.D., *Dangerous Marine Animals.* Cambridge, Md., Cornell Maritime Press, 1959.

Hylander, C. J., *Adventures with Reptiles.* New York, Julian Messner, Inc., 1962.

Leopold, Comm. R.S., MSC, USN, and Hathan, Lt. (JG) R.H., MSC, U.S. Naval Reserve, "An Evalution of the Mechanical Treatment of Snake Bite." *Military Medicine,* Vol. 120, No. 6 (June, 1957), p. 414.

———, and Huber, Lt. G.S., MSC, USN, "Ineffectiveness of Suction in Removing Snake Venom from Open Wounds." *U.S. Armed Forces Medical Journal,* Vol. XI, No. 6 (June, 1960) , p. 682.

McCollough, Newton C., M.D., "Venomous Snake Bite." *The Journal of the Florida Medical Association,* Vol. XLIX, No. 12 (June, 1963), p. 980.

———, and Gennaro, Joseph F., Jr., Ph.D., "Coral Snake Bites in the United States." *The Journal of the Florida Medical Association,* Vol. XLIX, No. 12 (June, 1963), p. 968.

———, "Evaluation of Venomous Snake Bite in Southern United States." *The Journal of the Florida Medical Association,* Vol. XLIX, No. 12 (June, 1963), p. 959.

———, "Summary of Snake Bite Treatment." *The Journal of the Florida Medical Association,* Vol. XLIX, No. 12 (June, 1963), p. 977.

Minton, Sherman A., Jr., M.D., "Observations on Amphibians and Reptiles of the Big Bend Region of Texas." *The Southwestern Naturalist,* (June, 1959), p. 28.

———, "Snakebite." *Diseases Due to Chemical Agents.*

———, "Snakebite in the Midwestern Region." *Quarterly Bulletin,* Indiana University Medical Center, Indianapolis, Ind., Vol. XIV, No. 2.

———, "Some Health Problems for the Medical Zoologist in the Big Bend Country." *Quarterly Bulletin,* Indiana University Medical Center, Indianapolis, Ind. (October, 1955).

———, "Variation in Venom Samples from Copperheads (*Agkistrodon contortrix mokeson*) and Timber Rattlesnakes (*Crotalus horridus horridus*)." *Copeia,* (November 27, 1953), p. 212.

———, "Venomous Animals, Spiders and Insects." *Pest Control Magazine,* (January-May, 1959).

———, and Anderson, Jeromie A., "Feeding Habits of the Kukri Snake, Oligodon Taeniolatus." *Herpetoligica,* Vol. XIX, No. 2 (July, 1963), p. 147.

———, and Bechtel, H. B., "Another Indiana Record of Cemophora Coccinea and a Note on Egg Eating." *Copeia,* (February 21, 1958).

Oliver, James A., *Snakes in Fact and Fiction.* New York, Doubleday Anchor Book, 1963.

Parrish, Henry M., M.D., D.P.H., "Analysis of 460 Fatalities from Venomous Animals in the United States." *The American Journal of the Medical Sciences,* Vol. 245, No. 2 (February, 1963), p. 129.

——, "Ophidiasis in Oklahoma." *The Journal of the Oklahoma State Medical Association* (June, 1964).

——, and Donovan, Louis P., M.S., "Bites by Poisonous Snakes in South Carolina." *Journal of the South Carolina Medical Association,* (February, 1964).

——, "Facts About Snakebites in Alabama." *Journal of the Medical Association of the State of Alabama,* Vol. 33, No. 10 (April, 1964), p. 297.

——, "Incidence of Poisonous Snakebites in Mississippi." *Journal of the Mississippi State Medical Association,* Vol. V, No. 6 (June, 1964), p. 222.

——, "On Poisonous Snakebites in Georgia." *Journal of the Medical Association of Georgia,* Vol. 53, No. 7 (July, 1964), p. 233.

——, Snakebite Accidents in Kentucky." *The Journal of the Kentucky State Medical Association,* (April, 1964).

——, "Survey of Snakebites in West Virginia." *The West Virginia Medical Journal,* Vol. 60, No. 6 (February, 1964), p. 143.

——, "Venomous Snakebites in Tennessee." *The Journal of the Tennessee Medical Association,* Vol. 57, No. 4 (April, 1964), p. 141.

Schmidt, Karl P., and Davis, Dwight D., *Field Book of Snakes of the United States and Canada.* New York, G.P. Putnam's Son, 1941.

Slater, James R., "A Key to the Adult Reptiles of Washington State." Occasional Papers, Dept. of Biology, University of Puget Sound, Tacoma, Washington, (August 30, 1963).

Sowder, Wilson T., M.D., M.P.H., and Gehres, George W., B.S., M.P.H., "Snakebites in Florida." *The Journal of the Florida Medical Association,* (June, 1963), p. 937.

Werler, John E., "Poisonous Snakes of Texas." Bulletin #31, Texas Parks and Wildlife Department, Austin, Texas, 1964.

Ya, Po M., M.D.; Guzman, Tomas, M.D.; and Perry, John F., M.D., "Treatment of Bites of North American Pit Vipers." *Southern Medical Journal,* Vol. 54, No. 2 (February, 1961), p. 134.

INDEX